FARTS
AREN'T
INVISIBLE

Also by Mick O'Hare

FARTS AREN'T INVISIBLE

Mind-blowing Facts From Science, History, Sport and the Universe

MICK O'HARE

Publishers

First published in the UK in 2023
by Bedford Square Publishers Ltd,
London, UK

bedfordsquarepublishers.co.uk
@bedsqpublishers

ISBN
978-1-915798-94-7 (Paperback)
978-1-915798-95-4 (eBook)

2 4 6 8 10 9 7 5 3 1

Printed in Great Britain by CPI Group (UK) Ltd, Croydon CR0 4YY

*Dedicated to Pierre Levegh – a racer to the end –
and all the victims of Le Mans 1955*

*With thanks, as ever, to Sally and Thomas.
Marathon*

CONTENTS

INTRODUCTION

Sometimes it is just being in the right place at the right time. In March, 1994, *New Scientist* kicked off its *Last Word* column asking readers for their everyday science questions. I happened to be in the eyeline of the boss, so he asked me to edit the new addition to the magazine.

There are huge scientific questions – how did the universe form, why is there only (as far as we know) life on Earth, and what the heck are we going to do about artificial intelligence? But this was not the remit of the *Last Word* column, which instead was devoted to everyday scientific trivia. We were frequently asked about farting, which gave inspiration to the book you are now holding. Although, I hasten to add, there's a whole lot more in here too. My quest for knowledge and seemingly trivial facts has never dimmed. It can turn you into a pub bore, it can make you look half-decent at *University Challenge*, but it's impossible to ignore that gnawing "I wonder why . . . ?". Perhaps you feel the same.

For me it's simply a way of looking at the world, mentally voicing a question, diving down the rabbit hole, and popping back up with the answer, plus another 10 things you found while you were down there. From the internet, from friends, from observation, and from experimentation, the more obscure, the better. And then storing it all away. Some of it is never used. Most of it, I fear, is forgotten. But some of it creeps into my consciousness and stays, a huge accumulation of information with no egress. You should try living in my head . . . *Does it hurt?* concerned friends ask. No, not really, but I can't rest until I have discovered the "who, what, why, where?" And it's been accumulating seemingly for aeons.

This book is an outlet for all those perplexing, intriguing, obscure (and yes, frequently inconsequential) facts. I carry a notebook, but mostly I ponder. As a child I watched Atlantic waves roll up a Cornish beach and saw that every so often two would combine and the water would rush further up the sand with the accumulated volume driving it on. It meant that you could predict when people near the water's edge would suddenly have to step back to avoid wet shoes. Everything you see or encounter is an opportunity to learn something.

Science is primarily about discovery, surely the driver of our species. Checking every available possibility and acting on the evidence. Facts are at the heart of science and I hope that you'll be entertained, amused, and slightly edified. Some of my rather arbitrary passions are on the following pages – early space exploration, gastronomy, human biology, and, strangely, the Le Mans 24-hour race (do go, if you ever get the chance). Eagle-eyed readers will, I hope, forgive the indulgence of revisited obsessions, leitmotifs from an earlier era – we are looking at you, Mr Bond, with your vodka martinis, and you, Dr MacDougall, foolishly attempting to weigh the human soul – but when new evidence comes to light, I make no apology for keeping atop of subjects of vital importance to humanity.

So here it is – the whole gamut from moon landings to the Monty Hall paradox. There's a saying in our family – often directed in mocking tones back at me – "I think you'll find . . . " You may find yourself uttering it after reading this book.

Mick O'Hare

PS I have done my best to wheedle out urban myths (except for the most irresistible, flagged as apocryphal) but do get in touch if you know better.

CHAPTER 1

FLATULENCE

Farts aren't invisible.

Well, perhaps not to everything. But they are generally invisible to humans. Thank goodness, you think, as you shiftily try to move to a different part of the room. But just because humans can't see them, that doesn't mean they are colourless. Humans can only see light that falls in the spectrum between the ultraviolet and infrared wavelengths. And because nearly every substance absorbs light, some gases absorb it at wavelengths we can't see. But beware, some animals such as frogs, snakes, and goldfish can see infrared. Goldfish can even see ultraviolet too. So if you're standing near your new date's bijou aquarium, don't be so certain you got away with it. The startled fish might report back later.

* * *

Farts can also be captured by thermal cameras, and anybody daring to eat too much broccoli or cabbage might produce enough sulphur in their gut to generate a visible cloud as it's expelled.

The average adult farts approximately 10 times a day, creating enough gas to inflate a party balloon.

Henry II of England once gave one of his minstrels (Roland le Fartere – yes, really) a 12-acre estate for being able to perform his annual Christmas party trick of a hop and a whistle, followed by a fart. Roland's descendants continued the tradition.

It's reputed that zebras' farts are the loudest (possibly apocryphal evidence suggests they can be heard five kilometres away).

Blue whales produce a fart bubble so big the aforementioned zebra could fit inside it.

In 2017 researchers at the University of Alabama released a definitive ledger of animals that can fart. Perhaps of greater interest is the ones that don't appear on the list. Crabs, parrots, and octopuses don't fart. Spiders and salamanders possibly do, while sea anemones don't – but apparently their burps smell dreadful.

Most fish don't fart, but instead package bubbles of waste gas (often ingested by surface feeding) into the gelatinous stools they deposit from their anuses.

Most farts contain odourless oxygen, nitrogen, carbon dioxide, hydrogen, and methane. But the rotten-egg odour is caused by hydrogen sulphide – created by the microbes acting on the food that is passing through your gut.

Beans make you fart because they contain carbohydrates known as oligosaccharides. Our bodies lack the enzymes to break these down, so the bacteria in our intestines do it for us. The by-product of that is gas. Smelly gas. But don't stop eating beans, as they are connected to a stronger immune system and better gastrointestinal health.

Foods that make you fart least include lean red meat, poultry, rice, quinoa, and oats.

Farts smell different in the bath because they are heated by the water as the gas passes through it, and the bubble also has less time to diffuse as it would in air, thus giving a concentrated hit to your nose as you sit above it. The fart gas may also exchange molecules with the heated water it passes through before reaching your nose, altering the odour.

Men fart more than women, but women's are smellier, which rather goes against the grain of anecdotal evidence.

Participants in an Australian trial had to record their farting in a diary. Men produced 12.7 farts a day, women 7.1. However, researchers in the US built on this earlier work by getting men and women to fart into a tube after eating pinto beans. Again, men farted more and produced more gas, but women's farts had a greater concentration of hydrogen sulphide.

And yes, you really can ignite farts. The methane they contain is highly inflammable, which is why I wouldn't recommend it. Rock musician Frank Zappa wrote about it in "Let's Make the Water Turn Black" and it did not end well for Ronnie and Kenny.

Farts are so combustible that up until the 1980s they were infrequently implicated in fatal bowel explosions during routine operations on the gastrointestinal tracts of patients.

While it's all subjective and hydrogen sulphide often appears atop lists of the world's smelliest substances, thioacetone, an organosulphur compound, has been reported capable of inducing vomiting, unconsciousness, and nausea for up to an 800-metre radius if exposed to air. As a result, it is regarded as a dangerous chemical, simply due to its awful smell and the reactions it causes.

Joseph Pujol, known by his stage name of Le Pétomane, was a French professional flatulist. His act consisted of farting in tune to music and making the sounds of musical instruments. He also did cannon fire and thunderstorms. There is argument, however, as to whether Pujol really farted because, instead of actually passing intestinal gas, he was capable of sucking air inwards through his anus and expelling it to order.

Research has shown that if one person farts alone, they do not smile or laugh. Farts are only amusing when two or more people are present, with the glee increasing in proportion to the number of people in attendance. Once the group reaches a certain size and people are less familiar with those present, then overt amusement once more dissipates. Sniggering replaces laughter.

At the 1976 Olympics East German swimmers had 1.8 litres of air pumped into their colons through their anuses in order to improve buoyancy. "Cheating through farting," wrote one West German newspaper. Later, in order to stop competitors having to clench their buttocks to hold the gas in, inflated condoms were attempted. Both failed to have the desired effect, because swimming speed relies on immersion in water rather than floating atop it.

The main gaseous constituents of (human) burps are odourless nitrogen and oxygen that are swallowed, collected in your oesophagus, and then expelled as you eat. If you've consumed a lot of fizzy drinks, carbon dioxide can be added to the mix. Burps are usually audible, unlike farts, which can be silent (see Myth Busting, below).

Astronauts have discovered that in zero gravity, stomach contents are not constrained by gravity. This means they routinely experience "sicky burps" or, in official NASA terminology, "wet burps".

There is a poo standard. It's called the Bristol Stool Scale and it has seven types running from "Separate hard lumps like nuts", through "Like a sausage but with cracks on the surface", to "Watery, no solid pieces, entirely liquid".

Poo is brown because of stercobilin, a by-product of broken-down red blood cells, and bile, used to digest fat. The ideal stool colour, according to gastroenterologists, is a "deep chocolatey colour, like melted chocolate". It should also sink to the bottom of the toilet.

The largest human turd ever recorded came from a Viking, who lived in York in England in the 9th century. It is 20 centimetres long and 5 centimetres wide, and was discovered semi-fossilised in an archaeological dig under a branch of Lloyds Bank. Detailed studies show that the owner ate a regular diet of bread and meat and suffered from worms. It is on display at York's Jorvik Viking Centre.

Fossilised turds are called coprolites. The largest ever discovered belonged to a *Tyrannosaurus Rex* dinosaur. It is 67.5 centimetres long and 15.7 centimetres wide and was found near Buffalo in South Dakota. Nicknamed Barnum, the fossilised poo is now owned by coprolite collector George Frandsen, who has about 1300 in his collection.

Our intestines are home to more than 2000 species of bacteria, a whopping 10 billion per cubic centimetre.

The biggest parasite that can live inside us is the 10-metre-long beef tapeworm.

Dogs poo in alignment with Earth's magnetic field. In 2013 scientists from the Czech Republic and Germany measured 1893 random canine defecations (and 5582 urinations) and concluded that dogs align their spines with the north-south magnetic field before dumping. More research is required to discover why.

MYTH BUSTING

Myth: Farts can cure cancer.

In 2014 tabloid newspapers reported that smelling farts could cure some fatal illnesses, including cancer. Cue lots of giggling and people collecting their farts in sealed bags. Researchers at the University of Exeter and the University of Texas had discovered that hydrogen sulphide could prevent damage to the mitochondria of human cells and preserve the cells' functions, meaning that there could be treatments for diseases involving cell damage, such as cancer or dementia. Because hydrogen sulphide is found in large quantities in farts, it was extrapolated that, when your partner farts, it might be wise to sniff it (or if you are single, sniff your own farts). However, the researchers had created a compound known as AP39, which delivers hydrogen sulphide specifically to the mitochondria. Outside sources, like sniffing gas from farts, would not have the same result. So that's good news or bad news, depending on your opinion of your partner's farts.

Myth: Silent farts are smellier than noisy ones.

It's not true, according to Michael Levitt, a gastroenter-ologist in Minneapolis, who has spent almost a lifetime studying flatulence. "Volume has nothing to do with it. It's down solely to what you have eaten and, secondarily, any infection you may be carrying," he asserts.

Myth: Thomas Crapper invented the flushing toilet.

The story goes that British plumber Crapper invented the toilets we all use today and therefore his name became synonymous with the act of using one. But flushing toilets were invented in 1596 by the Englishman Sir John Harington, a courtier of Queen Elizabeth I. His version used 28 litres for a single flush and had no S bend. The design was improved on by Scot Alexander Cumming, who introduced flush valves and patented his design. Thomas Crapper doesn't appear until the late 1880s, when he took out nine patents for different designs. It's possible that the word "crap" doesn't even derive from his name; it's more likely to come from the Latin word *crappa*, meaning chaff (or a waste product). Crapper's toilets did have his name on the side, however, which may have inspired or encouraged the slang usage.

CHAPTER 2

THE SOLAR SYSTEM AND THE UNIVERSE

You can still hear the remnants of the Big Bang.

All you need is a radio receiver. When our universe was formed from a single point in what is known as the Big Bang 13.8 billion years ago, it was super-hot. It has been expanding outwards and cooling ever since and, although space is now very cold, there is still leftover heat – known as the cosmic microwave background (CMB) – which can be detected by microwave telescopes as a glow pervading the whole sky. Unfortunately, it can't be seen by the naked eye because it is so cold, a mere 2.725 degrees above absolute zero (–273.15° Centigrade), but you can hear it, a genuine echo of the Big Bang. In 1964 astronomers Arno Penzias and Robert Wilson were using a radio antenna to measure signals from space and were puzzled by a sound they thought at first was just interference. But it was coming uniformly from all over the sky. They had detected the CMB and it won them the Nobel Prize for physics.

* * *

There's something missing from our universe. Well, it's not missing but we can't find it. Yet. Cosmologists have realised that all the stuff we can see in space, such as galaxies, is only a fraction of the mass of the universe. Something else is filling the gaps. We can't see it but we call it dark matter because it doesn't emit or absorb light. Its close cousin is called dark energy, which is causing the universe to expand faster, almost like the opposite of gravity. Dark matter matters because without it the universe doesn't work. It holds everything together like dough filling the gaps between currants in a bun. We know it's there because we can see it bending light from distant stars and it stops galaxies tearing themselves apart as they spin. One day we'll figure out what it is.

Black holes are so dense and therefore their gravity so strong that not even a ray of light can escape their clutches. Hence their name.

Neutron stars are very dense too. They are the remnants of giant stars that died in a fiery explosion known as a supernova. They have a mass of about twice that of our Sun and are the smallest and most dense stars known to exist. One teaspoon of material from a neutron star would have a mass of about 4 billion tonnes.

Our solar system is approximately 4.6 billion years old. The oldest planet is the giant blob of gas that constitutes Jupiter – twice as massive as all the other planets combined – which formed about 3 million years after the birth of the solar system.

Earth formed about 60 million years after the solar system began to coalesce (although some creationists wrongly believe that it's only around 6000 years old).

Earth is slowing down by about 1.7 milliseconds a century. Originally a day on Earth lasted only about six hours. Now, of course, it's 24. And the Moon is to blame. It creates the tides in our oceans, which bulge and create a twisting force that slows down the Earth's rotation.

Asteroids up to 50 metres in diameter, with some as big as 400 metres, pass between Earth and the Moon on average about once every two years. Small ones, a few metres in diameter, pass through several times a month.

The largest asteroid yet discovered is Ceres, 965 kilometres across. It was spotted in 1801, long before many of the solar system's planets. It accounts for more than a third of the mass of the asteroid belt that is located between Mars and Jupiter.

NASA's DART mission to adjust the orbit of an asteroid by crashing into it (useful if it is on a collision course with Earth) worked. In 2022 the spacecraft struck its target Dimorphos and reduced the time it took to orbit its parent asteroid Didymos, by 32 minutes.

One day on Venus lasts a whopping 5832 hours, or about 243 Earth days (which is longer than a year on Venus lasts – 225 days). Just because the planet rotates slowly on its axis doesn't mean it can't travel quickly around the Sun.

One day on Jupiter lasts only 9 hours 56 minutes, the shortest in our solar system.

Pluto's year is 90,520 Earth days (or 248 years), the longest in our solar system.

Venus is so inhospitable, with high temperatures of up to 475°C and an atmospheric pressure 90 times that of Earth, that when the Soviet Union's Venera spacecraft landed there between 1966 and 1983 their systems lasted mere minutes before the probes were melted or crushed.

All planets orbit the Sun in the same direction, but Venus is the only planet that, as it does so, rotates east to west, meaning that the Sun on Venus rises in the west.

Uranus rotates on its side, appearing to roll around the Sun like a ball.

The planet with the most moons is Saturn, with 145. It recently took the record from Jupiter (which has 92) in May 2023, when 62 new moons were discovered. But new moons are being discovered all the time. Jupiter may one day top the list again.

Mercury and Venus are the only two planets in our solar system with no moons.

The Sun takes up 99.86% of the mass of our solar system. However, it is very slowly losing mass as it produces energy.

1.3 million Earths, by volume, could fit inside the Sun. That's if you squished them up.

We know the universe is expanding because we can observe other galaxies speeding away from ours. In the same way an ambulance siren changes pitch after it passes us and its sound waves are stretched out, the same happens to light waves coming from galaxies. The waves are stretched and appear redder. The faster the galaxy is moving, the redder its light. This is known as "red shift".

If two pieces of metal touch in space they will permanently bond in a process known as cold welding. Merely the pressure of the metals touching in a vacuum is enough. On Earth, the atmosphere will always leave some molecules of air or water between the metal pieces, but in space these aren't present.

Sunlight takes 8 minutes 20 seconds to reach Earth.

In our solar system active volcanoes are only found on Earth and on Jupiter's moon Io. We know there are inactive volcanoes on Venus, Mars, Mercury, and our Moon. There may be active volcanoes on Venus and Jupiter's moon Europa, but we can't tell because Venus has dense cloud cover and Europa is covered in thick ice sheets.

Venus is the brightest planet in the solar system with an albedo of 0.75. Albedo is a measure of an object's reflectivity. By comparison the Earth's albedo is 0.305. Venus is so bright because its thick, sulphuric acid clouds reflect most of the sunlight it receives.

The biggest storm in the solar system is Jupiter's Great Red Spot, an elliptical-shaped anticyclone clearly visible on the surface of the planet, south of its equator. It has been raging for at least four centuries, has winds of up to 430 kilometres per hour and could fit about three Earth-size planets inside it. Saturn occasionally has more powerful storms but none are as enduring as the Great Red Spot. The spot does, however, appear to be shrinking.

The highest temperature on the Moon in direct sunlight can reach 120°C, the lowest at the poles and in shadow is −250°C. The lack of atmosphere means the warming effect from the Sun's rays is intense, but this same lack of atmosphere on the Moon and in space means there is no other warming effect. Once you are in shade, the temperature plummets. Similarly, when the Sun strikes the surface of a spacecraft, its surfaces expand rapidly while the shaded sides cool and contract. This can obviously lead to potential catastrophic structural defects, and it is why spacecraft always rotate during flight.

Are we all – animals and plants alike – descended from aliens? It's a theory, known as panspermia, that has waxed and waned over the centuries, but the suggestion is that bacteria or other microscopic life forms that evolved elsewhere in the universe could have been carried to Earth on meteorites, space dust, asteroids, and comets before evolving into higher forms of life. It's now a subject of serious scientific research. It seems microscopic organisms can survive the collisions necessary to be ejected from their host planet, travelling through the vacuum of space, and the impact of striking another planet. Which means your great-great-great-ancestor might have been a cold virus from the Andromeda galaxy. That's nothing to be sneezed at . . .

The first person to suggest the theory of panspermia was the 5th-century Greek philosopher, Anaxagoras. In the 20th century, to much scepticism, British astronomer Fred Hoyle and his protégé Chandra Wickramasinghe were modern-day proponents of the theory. Wickramasinghe would later prove that some interstellar dust was organic. Both believed that life forms continue to enter our atmosphere, giving rise to new diseases. Cue more sneezing . . .

Around two-thirds of the atoms in human bodies are hydrogen atoms that are almost as old as our universe (13.8 billion years old). However, hydrogen is very light, so this only accounts for about 10% of our mass. Most of the rest of the atoms in our bodies – mainly oxygen and carbon, but also including elements such as magnesium, nitrogen, calcium, and sulphur – were created inside stars by nuclear fusion reactions.

MYTH BUSTING

Myth: Space is a vacuum.

It isn't, at least not completely. It contains a low density of particles, thinly spread gases – mainly hydrogen and helium plasma – plus specks of dust. Every cubic metre will contain at least a few hundred molecules or atoms.

Myth: The Moon is made of green cheese.

Well, obviously it isn't. But it was once a piece of the Earth. This was proved by rock samples collected by the astronauts of Apollo 15 in 1971. It was most likely ejected from the Earth after it collided with another planetary object.

Myth: There are more stars in the Universe than grains of sand on Earth.

Author and cosmologist Carl Sagan made this claim in his book *Cosmos*. The online Math Dude Jason Marshall reckons that grains of sand outnumber stars because there are around 5 sextillion grains of sand on Earth (we don't have space to write all the zeros). Astronomer Bob Berman realised that Sagan was only referring to the Earth's beaches: if you include the deserts and sand on the seabed, sand wins out. It's still a lot of grains (or stars), mind you.

CHAPTER 3

HISTORY

The British are coming.

According to a book by historian Stuart Laycock – *All the Countries We've Ever Invaded (and the few we never got round to)* – published in 2012, there are only 22 countries in the world that have not been invaded, however briefly, by Britain: Andorra, Belarus, Bolivia, Burundi, Central African Republic, Chad, Republic of Congo, Guatemala, Ivory Coast, Kyrgyzstan, Liechtenstein, Luxembourg, Mali, Marshall Islands, Monaco, Mongolia, Paraguay, São Tomé and Principe, Sweden, Tajikistan, Uzbekistan, Vatican City. That's 22 out of 195. Other historians dispute the figure saying involvement, invitation, peacekeeping, or other political necessity does not necessarily amount to invasion.

Although Britain never invaded Monaco, Monaco did invade Britain. Along with ships from France and Genoa,

Monaco took part in an assault on Southampton as part of the English Channel Naval Campaign conducted by France during the early part of the Hundred Years' War.

The Hundred Years' War between England and France actually lasted 116 years (1337 to 1453).

* * *

Sumerian is regarded as the first human language, or at least the oldest written language, dating back to at least 2900 BC. It was used by people in Southern Mesopotamia and is an isolate language, which means it's not related to any other existing language.

However, Sumerian was almost certainly preceded by one or more proto-Afroasiatic languages – from western Asia and North Africa – which may date back 18,000 years.

Ancient Romans used stale urine as mouthwash, believing the small amount of ammonia it contained disinfected mouths and whitened teeth. Urine was being added to mouthwashes as late as the 18th century.

The year 46 BC was 445 days long because Julius Caesar had three leap months added to it to ensure that his new Julian calendar matched the seasons. It is – obviously – the longest year in history and was known as "the year of confusion".

Was Alexander the Great, king of ancient Macedonia, buried alive? From the descriptions of his symptoms, some historians believe he may have had Guillain-Barré syndrome which would have left him unable to move or communicate but mentally fully aware.

The University of Oxford (1096) is older than the Aztec Empire (its capital city was founded in 1325).

The longest war in history was the Reconquista, the military campaigns that kingdoms in the Iberian Peninsula waged against the occupying Moors from 711 until 1492 – that's 781 years.

The Anglo-Zanzibar War was the shortest war. Lasting about 38 minutes on 27 August 1896, it involved the Royal Navy firing on the Sultan of Zanzibar's palace after Zanzibar objected to Britain's choice of successor to the nation's throne.

Upmarket department store Fortnum & Mason on London's Piccadilly opened 69 years (1707) before the American declaration of independence (1776).

Archbishop Tenison's Church of England High School in Croydon, South London is the oldest surviving mixed-sex school in the world, dating back to 1714.

The inventor of the sandwich in the early 1760s was John Montagu, the Fourth Earl of Sandwich, who was an inveterate gambler. He refused to rise from his card table to eat, instead insisting his manservant bring salt beef wedged between two hunks of bread, so he could hold his food without getting greasy fingers as he played on and on. His aristocratic chums took note and began demanding "the same as Sandwich". And thus the snack was born. The earl was named after his family seat in the Kent town of Sandwich, chosen for the family's aristocratic title because it was a prominent seaport. Odd to think that, if he'd lived further north along the English coast, we might instead be eating Grimsbys.

Shrapnel is named after its inventor Henry Shrapnel, who served in the British army. In 1784 he invented a hollow cannonball filled with lead shot that would explode in mid-air.

Following his defeat in the wars since named after him, the French Emperor Napoleon Bonaparte was exiled to the island of St Helena in 1815. It's said that he took with him as his sole luxury a cask of cognac. The soldiers guarding him also appreciated drinking it and hence "Napoleon Brandy" was born. But according to some reports Napoleon was teetotal, so the story might be apocryphal.

In a study published in 1998 political scientists Dan Reiter and Allan Stam noted that, between 1816 and 1982, democracies won 76% of the wars they fought, while dictatorships won only 46%.

Since 1918, more than 1000 people have died in Belgium and France from unexploded bombs and shells left over from the First World War.

More people died in the Spanish flu pandemic in 1919 (possibly as many as 100 million) than died in the 1914–1918 First World War, which preceded it (possibly as many as 22 million, including civilians).

During the Second World War (1939–1945) 80% of all males who had been born in the Soviet Union in 1923 died.

Adolf Hitler's half-nephew fought against Germany in the Second World War. William Patrick Hitler, who was born in England (and rather unsurprisingly would later change his name to William Patrick Stuart-Houston) served in the US Navy through the war until 1947. He was awarded the Purple Heart and became a dual British-American citizen.

Researchers at the University of Austin estimate that 4% of the sand on the beaches of Normandy is comprised of ground-up shrapnel left over from the D-Day landings in 1944. The tiny grains of shrapnel can easily be picked up using a magnet.

North and South Korea have been at war since 1950. Although an armistice was negotiated between the two nations in 1953, no formal treaty was signed.

The first televised murder was that of Lee Harvey Oswald, the assassin of US President John F. Kennedy. He was shot in the stomach by nightclub owner Jack Ruby, as he was being transferred to a different prison from Dallas County Jail on 24 November, 1963. TV news cameras were covering Oswald's transfer.

The last use of the guillotine as a means of execution in France (10 September, 1977) postdated the release of the first *Star Wars* film (25 May, 1977).

UNESCO's World Atlas of Languages states that there are around 7000 living languages in the world. While only around 200 are spoken in Europe, the nation of Papua New Guinea speaks around 830, possibly more.

One third of the world's languages have fewer than 1000 speakers.

Paakyanti is one of the Aboriginal languages of Australia. In 2012 it was reported that only 24 people (at most) spoke it, and only two of them fluently. However, it has been reintroduced to schools in an attempt to save it.

Almost seven million people died in the recent Covid-19 pandemic, one of the deadliest in history. The World Health Organization declared coronavirus was no longer a global health emergency on 5 May, 2023.

MYTH BUSTING

Myth: Marie Antoinette said "Let them eat cake."

The story goes that Marie Antoinette, the Austrian-born queen of France during the French Revolution, when told the population was starving because there was no bread to eat, said, "Let them eat cake" instead. This proved that she was oblivious to the impoverished lives of ordinary French people. However, the quote was mistranslated into English from the French, which was originally "Let them eat brioche." Brioche is a sweetened bread, which in the 18th century was not the luxurious foodstuff we know today. Not only that, it is doubtful she ever uttered either phrase. It was more likely a common folklore story that had been doing the rounds in Europe for decades, if not centuries, and was repurposed as propaganda by revolutionaries wishing to make a point. Whether she said it or not, she still got the chop . . .

Other historical quotes misattributed:

Niccolò Machiavelli, the Italian diplomat and writer, never said, "The end justifies the means." He argued that one must consider the final result of any action, which isn't necessarily the same thing.

"There are only two certainties in life: death and taxes," said statesman and polymath **Benjamin Franklin**. Except he didn't say it first; 18th-century English actor and dramatist Christopher Bullock did.

"The death of one man is a tragedy, the death of millions is a statistic" might have encapsulated genocidal autocrat **Joseph Stalin**'s philosophy, but he was only repeating a dark satirical comment made by German writer Kurt Tucholsky.

The crew of ill-fated **Apollo 13** never said, "Houston, we have a problem." First, command module pilot Jack Swigert said, "OK, Houston, we've had a problem here", which was then repeated by commander Jim Lovell who said, "Uh, Houston, we've had a problem." But the truth rather spoils a million clichés since.

Myth: Someone who can't use their iPhone is a Luddite.

In modern parlance, if you can't navigate your way around Instagram, the insult du jour is that you're a Luddite, ignorant of modern technology. But the original Luddites understood modern technology all too well; they just didn't like it, because it was about to put them out of work. The Industrial Revolution saw huge factories replacing what were once local artisan endeavours. And the artisans weren't happy. So they set out to damage the new machines that were taking away their livelihoods. Perhaps the most notorious crackdown on their activities came on 11 April, 1812, when 100 workers marched on Rawfolds Mill in Liversedge, West Yorkshire. Fourteen of them would later hang at York over the course of one morning. It was the biggest judicial killing for a single crime in English history.

The Luddites were named after Ned Ludd, an apprentice who, so the story goes, began destroying machinery in Nottinghamshire in 1779. Ludd later turned out to be fictional.

The Tolpuddle Martyrs, six agricultural Labourers deported to Australia in 1834 for joining a trade union, were all later pardoned and returned to England. Despite their greater notoriety, they fared better than the West Yorkshire Luddites.

Myth: The town of Berwick-upon-Tweed was at war with Russia.

Berwick is a town in Northern England, right on the Scottish border, and was, for centuries, the source of much dispute between both nations. At the start of British involvement in the Crimean War in 1854, Queen Victoria, taking note of the tensions over Berwick, signed the declaration on behalf of "Victoria, Queen of Great Britain, Ireland, Berwick-upon-Tweed, and the British Dominions beyond the sea". But when the treaties ending the war were signed in 1856, everybody forgot about Berwick, meaning the town remained at war with Russia and/or the Soviet Union until somebody noticed the error in the 20th century, whereupon in 1966 a Russian diplomat visited Berwick, met a town councillor, and the two of them declared peace. The councillor, Robert Knox, reputedly said, "Please tell the Russian people that they can now sleep peacefully in their beds." It's a great tale, but sadly seems to be untrue. When the British Foreign Office investigated the story, the original documentation made no mention of Berwick, and there is no confirmed record of the 1966 visit.

Myth: Vikings had horned helmets.

No, they didn't. They only became associated with Vikings during the 19th century, when lots of operas were being written about Norse invaders and directors decided horned helmets looked the part.

Myth: The bomb the Dambusters used in the Second World War to destroy dams bounced along the water.

It didn't, according to Peter Johnston, curator and historian at the Imperial War Museum in Duxford, even though it was dubbed the bouncing bomb. "It skimmed or ricocheted off the water surface. It didn't bounce," he says. Its inventor Barnes Wallis was inspired both by watching children skimming stones across a lake and the 16th-century Royal Navy tactic of "bouncing" cannonballs off the surface of the sea. "And," adds Johnston, "it wasn't actually a bomb, it was a mine."

CHAPTER 4

LIFE ON EARTH

Whale "vomit" is used in making perfumes.

Sperm whales like eating squid, but they can't digest their beaks and pens. This means they sometimes accumulate in the whale's gut, where they form a solid mass saturated with faeces to protect the intestines from the sharp beaks. This slowly breaks down to form a cement-like slurry known as ambergris. Whale "vomit" is probably the wrong term, because it seems the ambergris is passed out through the whale's anus and, because it's buoyant, it rises to the surface where it bobs around until it's picked up by humans who use it in perfume-making.

It's estimated that only 1% of the world's sperm whales ever produce any ambergris. It is usually black and stinks to high heaven, but as it hardens over time the fragrance changes to a more "alluring" musky, agricultural aroma, which is the star attraction for perfumers.

It was used in early Arabic civilisations as medicine, incense, and even as an aphrodisiac.

If you find a chunk of ambergris on the beach, you are lucky. Good examples can fetch tens of thousands of pounds.

Due to its rarity and cost, synthetic chemicals often replace ambergris in modern perfumes.

* * *

Wombats have square poo. They do, they do, they do. And they manage to squeeze out 100 of them on an average day. Ouch! (OK, the corners are slightly rounded.) It's all to do with the elasticity of their intestines. Researchers at Georgia's Institute of Technology in the US found the muscles at the end of a wombat's gut drag the poo back and forth, removing liquid. This forms 2-centimetre-wide turds with a square cross-section. The evolutionary benefit is that the poo doesn't roll away and can be stacked, allowing the depositor to communicate with and attract other wombats.

Some species of electric eel can deliver a shock of up to 860 volts. That's more than three times the current in the UK mains supply and, if you are unfortunate, enough to kill you.

Elephants are the only four-legged mammal to have all four knees facing forwards. Every other one has at least one pair of legs that face backwards.

Only two mammals lay eggs: the duck-billed platypus and the echidna. These and other similar species, known as monotremes, once dominated the Australian continent but were usurped by marsupials such as kangaroos, koalas and wombats (doubtless showing off with their square poo).

While it seems intuitive that chimpanzees and orang-utans might have similar fingerprints to humans, koalas also have prints that appear almost identical and, like humans, are unique to each individual. It's an example of convergent evolution – different species developing similar traits independent of each other.

Farmers in Queensland avoid letting their sheep eat the leaves of browse trees (*Leucaena glauca*) because it makes them go bald. The trees contain mimosine, which stops cells in hair follicles working correctly, and the sheep shed their wool within 10 days.

The largest mammal on Earth is the blue whale (in fact, it is the largest animal ever to have lived – take that, dinosaurs). Females can weigh up to 150 tonnes and exceed 30 metres in length – more than the length of two London double-decker buses.

Conversely, the smallest mammal by weight is the Etruscan shrew, which lives in North America. It can be as short as 35 millimetres long and weigh as little as 1.5 grams. A British 1 penny coin weighs 3.5 grams.

The Etruscan shrew has an extinct rival. At an estimated 1.3 grams, the shrew-like *Batadonoides vanhouteni* was even lighter. It lived in North America more than 50 million years ago.

Songbirds have accents. In 2011 biologists discovered that birds in towns and cities have higher-pitched songs than countryside birds. Apparently, it's to do with their song echoing off buildings in urban areas and changing the tone. Birds also have different songs, depending on where they live. This was first spotted by Peter Barer, a British behavioural scientist, who realised that chaffinches sounded different from valley to valley. Their songs were similar but possessed a dialect.

Later, scientists found that some – but not all – birds learn their song from their parents and other adult birds. If the chicks were kept in isolation, they never learnt and just made the bird equivalent of "baby babble" for their whole lives.

According to fleascience.com, fleas (which on average weigh less than a gram) can jump as far as 48 centimetres at 6.8 kph, or more than 100 times their length. If a flea was a human long-jumper, it would be able to leap over the grandstands and outside an Olympic stadium.

The longest caterpillar in the world is the hickory horned devil of the eastern United States. It can grow to 15 centimetres.

The white witch moth of Central and Southern America has the largest wingspan of any insect in the world. One specimen was verified at 30.8 centimetres, although potentially larger individuals have been spotted.

The white witch moth, however, would be dwarfed by the griffin flies of the late Carboniferous period. Fossils of these insects show a wingspan of around 75 centimetres.

The desert locust, mainly found in Africa and Asia, is generally regarded as producing the largest swarms. A single swarm can cover up to 1200 square kilometres and can contain up to 80 million locusts per square kilometre, with a grand total of around 50 to 100 billion locusts. That's a combined weight of 200,000 tonnes.

The biggest recorded locust swarm, however, occurred in the US Midwest in 1885. It covered more than 500,000 square kilometres – more than double the size of the UK – and blocked out the sun for a week.

Blow flies have a sense of smell that can detect a dead animal carcass 1.5 kilometres away. They usually arrive at a new corpse within 10 minutes. Forensic scientists use blow flies to determine the time of death in human bodies by counting the number of eggs laid and the number of lifecycles the flies have passed through to calculate how long a body has been in situ.

The longest walrus tusk was 96.2 centimetres long, discovered in Alaska in 1997.

Narwhal tusks are hollow and can exceed 3 metres.

There are around 1200 venomous fish on Earth but the stonefish is the most lethal; its toxin can kill an adult human in less than an hour.

The deepest fish ever recorded was an unknown species discovered in 2022, when it was filmed at a depth of 8336 metres in an ocean trench near Japan. It is a tadpole-shaped species of snailfish and is translucent. It's believed that, because of the pressure, fish cannot live below 8400 metres.

The largest recorded animal eaten by a snake was an unfortunate 68-kilogram hyena, consumed by an African rock python. The encounter was filmed by *National Geographic* in 2017.

According to the International Union for Conservation of Nature, 42,108 of Earth's species are at risk of extinction.

Plants make up 40% of the total with the most at-risk animal groups being amphibians, mammals, and corals.

There are more tigers in captivity in the US (around 5000) than there are in the wild worldwide (around 4500).

The oldest verified known tree in the world was a Great Basin bristlecone pine known as Prometheus which was cut down in Wheeler Peak, Nevada in 1964. According to its rings, it was at least 4862 years old.

Plants may scream when damaged or starved of water. The frequency is too high for humans to detect but research in the journal *Cell* in 2023 noted that ultrasonic "popping" sounds were detected coming from plants that were suffering drought. They increased as the damage worsened.

The longest land migration by any animal is undertaken by caribou living in North America, northern Europe and Siberia. They can travel up to 1200 kilometres.

However, some wolves move more in a year than caribou do, it's just that they are not migrating. One grey wolf in Mongolia was GPS-tracked travelling 7247 kilometres in one year. That's like walking from Los Angeles to Washington DC.

Humpback whales migrate around 8000 kilometres non-stop as they move from their summer feeding grounds in cold, krill- and fish-rich seas to warmer waters in order to raise calves and avoid predation by killer whales.

No migration, however, can match that of the Arctic tern. Twice a year they fly between the Earth's polar regions, clocking up a minimum of 40,000 kilometres (and they only weigh around 100 grams).

MYTH BUSTING

Myth: Lemmings commit mass suicide.

Lemmings are small rodents that live in or around the Arctic tundra. Unbeknown to them, humans think that every few years, when their population becomes unsustainable, they all charge to the nearest Norwegian cliff and throw themselves off. While it's true that if a population in one area becomes too large for the food supply to sustain it, a large group will head off elsewhere in a pack, they, like any half-intelligent animal, would baulk at jumping off a cliff. And that's because they don't. But the real reason we think they do is down to an act of supreme cruelty. When the makers of the 1958 Disney nature film *White Wilderness* were looking for dramatic material, they happened upon a colony of unfortunate lemmings, and began chucking them off a cliff while they filmed. Truly shocking and, presumably because nobody believed anybody would actually do such a dreadful thing simply to make a documentary, the legend has endured. The footage has since been used by directors of political adverts as a metaphor for voting for the "wrong" party.

For such a small creature, lemmings have generated a preponderance of myths. For a long time people believed that lemmings spawned in the sky and then fell to Earth like rain, possibly because they appear very suddenly when they migrate to a new area. Another myth was that if you make a lemming angry – and they are quite irascible – it will explode. Again this might be attributable to migration. Any animals dying en route might expand as a result of gases that build up via methane-producing bacteria in the decomposing body, leading to explosive rupture.

Myth: Sharks need to keep swimming to stay alive and so can never sleep.

Water needs to constantly pass over the gills of sharks so that they can breathe. This has led to the belief that they need to move forward throughout their lives. But it's not true. Some species pass water over their gills using a pumping motion in their pharynx. And as long as the oceans have currents, water will ebb and flow, meaning some sharks can get away with stopping for a nap after being nasty to everything else in the sea.

Sharks, however, do not have a swim bladder, meaning that if they stop swimming they sink. They counteract this by having an oily, and therefore buoyant, liver, coupled with extraordinarily powerful pectoral fins, which allow them to swim in any direction, up or down.

Sharks don't have bones, unlike most fish. They belong to the subclass elasmobranchs, whose skeletons are composed of cartilage.

Myth: It is aerodynamically impossible for a bumblebee to fly.

Quite obviously it isn't, but it's been a long-standing urban (or perhaps pastoral) legend. It seems to have arisen in the 1930s, when French entomologist Antoine Magnan looked at the plump body of a bumblebee and decreed that this large, unaerodynamic insect could not be carried aloft by such tiny wings. Hence a bumblebee "cannot fly". However, any object with wings can fly if it can flap them fast enough to generate lift. Bumblebees flap theirs at very high speeds – about 230 times a second – and they have four of them, which gives incredible lift. They also flap them back and forth, not up and down, creating vortices. These vortices are like the eyes of hurricanes – they have lower pressure, which lifts the bee upwards. And if you think it's still implausible just watch . . . bumblebees fly.

Myth: The fastest creature on Earth is a cheetah.

The late raconteur Peter Ustinov used to tell the story of how, when he was a schoolboy, the teacher used to demand facts from his pupils (he needed this book). Name a Russian composer, he demanded of the young Ustinov. "Er, Nikolai Rimsky-Korsakov", he replied. "Nonsense boy, it's Tchaikovsky, everybody knows that," snorted the teacher. So, what's the fastest animal on Earth? The peregrine falcon. Nonsense, everybody knows it's the cheetah. Except it isn't. The cheetah is the fastest land mammal but it only reaches 112 kilometres per hour (kph). The peregrine falcon tops out at 390 kph. In fact the fastest fish – the sailfish – can almost match a cheetah's speed at 110 kph, while the fastest flying insect is the dragonfly at 56 kph. However, the fastest animal in relation to its body size is a Californian mite. *Paratarsotomus macropalpis* is the size of a poppy seed and can clock speeds of up to 320 body lengths per second, which is more than 100 of its tiny steps. That would mean, if it were human, it could run at more than 2000 kph (or Mach 1.6). The top speed for a fit human running is around 36 kph, which means even Usain Bolt wouldn't stand a chance against *Paratarsotomus*. Unless he stood on it, of course.

Paratarsotomus macropalpis can also withstand temperatures of up to 60°C.

If you want to play devil's advocate, this one's for you. All animals on Earth are travelling faster than a peregrine falcon. Our planet orbits the Sun at more than 100,000 kph and because we all live on it . . .

Myth: Ostriches bury their heads in the sand when threatened.

It's even given us an everyday idiom. We bury our heads in the sand when we don't want to acknowledge a problem. But ostriches don't do it. What they do is lay their eggs in shallow holes and turn them several times a day using their beaks. This may have led to the myth. So what do they do if they see a predator? They run. Very quickly. An ostrich has a top speed of around 70 kph.

Myth: The piranha fish has the sharpest teeth of any animal.

It's actually the orca, or killer whale, which isn't a fish at all, but an ocean-dwelling mammal (for that matter, it's not a whale either, it's a species of dolphin). It also dispels another myth – it, not the crocodile, has the most powerful bite of any animal, uncorroborated, but possibly as high as 1335 kilogram-force per square centimetre (kg/cm^2). By comparison, the saltwater crocodile's bite generates around 281 kg/cm^2, and a human's a mere 11.5 on average.

However, during a research test at the University of Florida in 1986 Richard Hofmann achieved a bite strength of 68.5 kg/cm^2 for approximately two seconds.

Myth: Penguins only live in cold climates.

Untrue. The Galapagos penguin (*Spheniscus mendiculis*) lives near the equator on the eponymous islands. Temperatures on the Galapagos Islands usually range between 21 and 30°C. Today, there are fewer than 1000 breeding species of the penguin.

The smallest penguin is the Antipodean fairy penguin (*Eudyptula minor*) which is 40 centimetres in length and weighs about a kilogram.

Myth: Ducks' quacks don't echo.

Where the heck this came from we have no idea but it's a widely circulated urban myth. Take it from us, put a couple of ducks in a cave, give them something to chat about, and there'll be quite an echo-induced cacophony.

Myth: Goldfish have a memory span of 1 second.

Nope. Experiments have shown that goldfish can remember things for long periods. Goldfish often know they are about to be fed when they see humans approaching their tank or pond, while goldfish that are fed from a green food box while a similar red one remains empty congregate around the green box even if the boxes are moved to different locations. Goldfish also learn to gather at the bottom of ponds if predators are present.

CHAPTER 5

FOOD

Farmed salmon aren't pink.

That's because the diet they consume in fish farms would leave them a less palatable grey. But when you buy them in the supermarket, miraculously they are a pleasant pink colour, the same as wild salmon. Salmon farmers add carotenoids – red pigmenting compounds – to their feed to provide them with the hue customers expect.

* * *

Swiss cheese has become less "holey". It's true. And it's all down to modern levels of hygiene. Swiss cheeses such as Emmenthal contain a particular subspecies of *Propionibacterium*, a bacterium that produces carbon dioxide. In the past, the cheese frequently contained microscopic specks of hay that fell from the dairy cattle as their milk was being collected in buckets. Thanks to surface tension, the carbon dioxide given off by the bacteria clumped around these specks and formed bubbles, known as eyes, in the solidifying cheese. The transition from old-fashioned milking methods in barns to automated, industrial systems has meant less hay is falling into the milk, and the holes in Swiss cheese have been getting smaller. Scientists have suggested adding hay dust to the milk if the holes continue to shrink. Watch this space, errrr . . .

Is there a Single Gloucester cheese? Yes. Most people have heard of Double Gloucester but there is a Single Gloucester too. Double Gloucester is aged for longer and is smoother but the origin of the two names is unsure. It could be because in the past the milk had to be skimmed twice to make the Double variety, or because cream from milking the cows in the morning was added to cream from evening milking. Or it could be as boring as a Double Gloucester cheese round being twice the size of a single. Conversely, if you want to find out if there is a double malt whisky, head over to page 90.

Foods you (or some people) eat alive: oysters (obviously), snakes (most often in Vietnam), fish and octopus (most often in Japan), Yin Yang fish (deep-fried – but still living! – in Taiwan), the gonads of sea urchins (in a rather surprising number of countries).

In the South Korean dish Sannakji, an octopus is killed and immediately served sliced into smaller pieces.

Because its nerves still have activity after death, its tentacles continue to squirm on the plate. If incorrectly sliced, the octopus's suction cups can stick to the inside of a diner's throat, suffocating the individual.

Former French President Mitterrand's last supper was an ortolan, a tiny songbird, drowned in brandy, roasted rapidly, and with the diner's face covered by a napkin, swallowed whole. The ortolan is an endangered species and eating it is now outlawed in the EU.

Figures from 2022 show that 22% of the world's population is vegetarian.

India has more vegetarians than any other nation. According to some estimates as many as 42% of the population is vegetarian, more than double the next country on the list, Mexico, with 19%.

Russia is the world's least vegetarian nation. Only 1% of the population eschews meat.

The hotness of chilli peppers is measured in Scoville Heat Units (SHUs). The hottest chilli in the world is the Carolina Reaper, which has 2.2 million SHUs. The average supermarket chilli comes in at around 250 SHUs.

SHUs are a measure of how many capsaicinoids a pepper has. Standard bell peppers have almost none.

Peppers contain more vitamin C than orange juice.

The space inside a bell pepper contains similar gases to air, plus a bit more ethylene produced by the plant. However, the relative amounts of the gases found in air differ inside a pepper. Researchers discovered the gas inside was 49% nitrogen, 29% oxygen, 4% argon, and 17% carbon dioxide. In contrast, the air surrounding the pepper is 78% nitrogen, 21% oxygen, 1% argon, and 0.04% carbon dioxide.

The most popular cheese in the world is Cheddar. It was first made in 12th-century England but is now made worldwide.

The United States is the world's biggest cheese producer (around 6,350,000 tonnes in 2022) but per head of population the French eat the most cheese: 26.2 kilograms per person per year.

According to Interpol, cheese is the most stolen foodstuff in the world: 4% of all cheese produced gets nicked!

Smell my cheese, inexplicably screamed Steve Coogan's comedic character Alan Partridge during a deranged moment in a restaurant. Maybe he'd been eating Epoisse de Bourgogne from France, generally recognised as the world's smelliest cheese. It's so pungent it's been banned from public transport . . .

The blue in cheese is caused by *Penicillium roqueforti* fungus and, as the fungus's name might suggest, the world's bluest cheese is considered to be Roquefort. The fungus grows naturally in the caves of south-west France where the cheese is produced but it can be added artificially to make other blue cheeses such as Stilton and Gorgonzola.

All of which leads us nicely on to the world's most disgusting cheese. And no, it isn't subjective. Casu Marzu from Sardinia uses live maggots in its production. It's banned in the USA and the European Union – although you can still find it in parts of Sardinia and Corsica – because eating the maggots can cause lesions in the digestive tract. We suggest you give it a miss.

However awful Casu Marzu sounds (or is), probably the most disgusting food in the world is kiviak from Greenland. A disembowelled seal is stuffed with small Arctic birds called Alle Alle. It is then sewn shut, buried and left to ferment for up to 18 months, after which the birds are removed. Kiviak is eaten by biting off the bird's head and then sucking out the juices inside, although the birds can also be eaten whole, bones and all. Disgusting it may sound but the preservation method helped Greenlanders survive harsh winters and food shortages in years past.

Kiviak, however, doesn't smell as bad as Surströmming from Sweden. This is fermented Baltic sea herring and, according to Malmö's Disgusting Food Museum, is the dish that induces the most vomiting among visitors.

According to the museum, ranking foods into a league table is difficult. Some people are put off by the smell, others by the presence of flies or maggots, others by decay. However, it rates Surströmming as probably the most foul, closely followed by Korean Ttongsul, which uses the poo of a human child mixed with rice and left to ferment until it forms an alcoholic drink. Which, of course, stinks!

Black pudding is in the Malmö museum. Some cultures find a dish made of pig's blood quite appalling.

One in four hazelnuts ends up in a jar of Nutella.

In 1908 legendary French chef Auguste Escoffier served "thighs of dawn nymphs" at his restaurant at the Savoy Hotel in London because he thought the English would baulk at eating frogs' legs.

The tomato is considered a fruit by botanists and a vegetable by nutritionists.

You can hear rhubarb growing. Visit the darkened rhubarb-forcing sheds of West Yorkshire and you'll hear a creaking sound. That's the rhubarb growing towards the light.

Nutmeg is hallucinogenic. You'd have to consume a lot to feel its effects but it contains myristicin, which interacts with signalling pathways in the human body. Myristicin is also an effective insecticide.

Cheese crackers have holes in them to stop air bubbles blowing them apart during the baking process.

The formula for boiling an egg is:

$$t_{cooked} = \frac{M^{2/3}c\rho^{1/3}}{K\pi^2(4\pi/3)^{2/3}}\log_e\left[0.76 \times \frac{(T_{egg} - T_{water})}{(T_{yolk} - T_{water})}\right]$$

I shall elaborate no further, except to say that it's probably simpler to put the egg in a pan of boiling water for three and a half minutes.

In 1644, Lord Protector of England and religious fanatic Oliver Cromwell banned pie eating, which he decreed to be a pagan pleasure. The ban was lifted in 1660, when the British monarchy was restored under Charles II.

A single spaghetti stick is called a spaghetto.

The margherita pizza isn't just a bread base with tomato and mozzarella on top. It should also have basil leaves too, so that the three foodstuffs represent the colours of the Italian flag. It's possibly named after Queen Margherita of Savoy and was first served in Naples in 1889 by chef Raffaele Esposito.

Hawaiian pizza has been voted the most controversial pizza in an Italian study. Purists say pineapple should never be found on a pizza. Others say they agree, but rather like it. It also wasn't invented in Hawaii. It was an invention of Sam Panopoulos of the Satellite restaurant in Ontario, Canada.

Pineapples can take up to three years to grow. That Hawaiian pizza wasn't made overnight.

Pizza (Hawaiian or otherwise) is the most popular dish in the world.

MYTH BUSTING

Myth: Asparagus makes your pee smell.

And it's pretty pungent. We all know that, don't we? Well, some of us don't (and not just those who don't like asparagus). As many as 60% of the population are genetically incapable of picking up the odour. And the smell (if you can smell it) is caused by methanethiol, dimethyl disulphide and dimethyl sulphone. As much of a mouthful as a bunch of green veg.

If you can't smell the asparagus don't be too disappointed. Here are some other foods that make your pee odorous: chicken (especially deep-fried), corned beef, coffee, broccoli, garlic, onions, Brussels sprouts, fish, cumin, pine-apple (one of the few that actually improves the smell).

Myth: Eating cheese before bedtime gives you nightmares.

It's not the cheese eating, it's the late eating what does it. Fatty foods, like cheese, take longer to digest. Having a full stomach leads to disturbed sleep. When you are lying down, the normal action of gravity on your digestive tract is disturbed. An argument has been put forward that cheese contains tyramine, which can release noradrena-line – a neurotransmitter – into your brain. But other foodstuffs contain this too and they do not have cheese's nocturnal reputation. Rule of thumb: organise your cheese-and-wine parties early because . . .

Alcohol, however, really does disturb your sleep, inter-rupting normal sleep cycles, inhibiting deep sleep, and – as you'll no doubt have discovered – it makes you want to get up to use the toilet.

Myth: Eating celery consumes more calories than the celery itself possesses.

This is still being argued over. A stick of celery contains something between six and ten calories. Moving your jaw to chew it takes up no more than one. Such "negative-calorie" foods also include grapefruit, broccoli, and lettuce, but the only way to make them work in your favour would be to chew them for several hours before swallowing. Unpalatable at best.

The fact that all humans can lose weight means, in effect, that any food could be described as "negative-calorie". If you put in the effort through exercise to burn more calories than you consume, you will lose weight. But it's far simpler to go out for a walk than to chew a stick of celery for ten hours.

Myth: Sir Walter Raleigh first brought potatoes to England.

And for that matter it wasn't Sir Francis Drake either. Actually it was Sir Thomas Harriott who imported them from Virginia in 1586.

Myth: You either love or hate Marmite.

Apparently 27% of people don't care either way. I salute their indifference.

CHAPTER 6

MATHEMATICS

Why you should change your mind.

Here's a conundrum. It's known as the Monty Hall problem because the US TV show with a similar scenario called *Let's Make a Deal* was hosted by Monty Hall. You're taking part in a game show. There are three doors, behind one of which is a new car. Choose the wrong box, though, and you win nothing. You have a one in three chance. You select Door 1. The game show host keeps it closed but opens Door 3, which he knows has nothing behind it. So now you are left with two choices. The host asks if you want to stick with your original selection or switch to Door 2. It seems like it's a 50/50 choice. The car is either behind Door 1 or Door 2. Surely it makes no difference if you change from your original choice. Except, astonishingly, it does. If you change to Door 2, you improve your chances of winning to two in three. But how? When you make your first choice, you have a one in three chance of being correct. But when the host opens one of the remaining doors, he knows that either you have chosen the correct door already (but you only have a one in three chance of doing that) or more likely you haven't (because your chance of doing so was only one in three). So if, as is statistically likely, the car is behind one of the two remaining doors that you didn't choose in the first place, he will open the one (Door 3) that doesn't have the car behind it, meaning that the door he didn't open (Door 2) is more likely to be hiding the car. You may still lose out by switching your choice, but your chances are greatly improved if you do.

What, you ask? OK. Try it this way:

If the car is behind Door 1, then he will reveal that there is nothing behind one of the two remaining doors. If you stick with Door 1, you win. **If you switch, you lose.**

If the car is behind Door 2, then when you choose Door 1, the host is forced to reveal that there is nothing behind Door 3. If you stick with Door 1, you lose. **If you switch, you win.**

If the car is behind Door 3, then when you choose Door 1, the host is forced to reveal nothing behind Door 2. If you stick with Door 1, you lose. **If you switch, you win.**

So, as you can see from the examples above, switching results in a win two out of three times. Think about it. You have turned your original odds of one in three into a two in three chance. It all rests on the fact that your initial choice was likely to be incorrect, so you are effectively forcing your host to tell you where the car is more likely to be.

Yet another way to look at it is from your own perspective as the contestant. If you switch, you might get it wrong. But now you know your odds are one in two, whereas when you made your initial choice, your odds were much worse at one in three and you probably chose one of the wrong doors. Or, in other terms, you don't know whether your first choice is right or wrong, but it's most likely to have been wrong so, if you switch, your new choice is more likely to be right. The host has improved your chances by opening Door 3 because he is in the know.

The problem was popularised in the early 1990s by Marilyn vos Savant. Pompous mathematicians derided the theory until tests using this system, some of them carried out by schoolteachers and their pupils across the USA, proved her to be correct. If you carry out her instructions, you have a two in three, or 66.6% chance of winning, rather than a one in three (33.3%).

And if you are still unsure, do what a scientist would do and try it for yourself with family or friends, say, 20 times. Then you'll realise it's true.

* * *

Another counterintuitive fact is that if you have a random group of just 23 people, there is a 50-50 chance that two of them will share the same birthday. It's known as the birthday paradox. It seems unlikely but when you consider that the birthday comparisons are made between every possible pair of individuals present, that gives us 253 chances for matching birthdays. How so? Well the first person has 22 comparisons to make, but the second person was already compared to the first person, so they have 21 comparisons to make. The third person then has 20 comparisons, the fourth person has 19 and so on. If you add up all possible comparisons (22 + 21 + 20 + 19 + ... +1) the sum is 253 comparisons. So each group of 23 people involves 253 chances for matching birthdays.

If you increase the number of people in the room to 75, the chances of two sharing the same birthday increases to 99%.

The British standard for providing toilet facilities at mass spectator events is one urinal per man and one WC cubicle for women, per 25 attendees of each gender. There is also an additional cubicle per 250 men, taking into account the fact that most people visit the toilet to urinate, not defecate.

Studies have shown that, if there are five urinals in a men's toilet, they are most usually filled in the order (where urinal 1 is nearest the entrance door) 1, 5, 3, 2, and 4. The same almost applies to cubicles in women's toilets except they fill in the order 5, 1, 3, 4, and 2, clearly showing women's preference for being further away from the door (or that men are lazier).

Depending on the source, around a million people are estimated to be flying in aircraft at any one time, which is the equivalent of about 65,000 tonnes of human.

The orange group of properties on a standard Monopoly board are statistically the most likely spots for players to land on when they get out of jail. So, if you want to charge your opponents lots of rent, buy those.

Struggle to convert between Centigrade and Fahrenheit? Just remember to reverse the digits: 16°C is about 61°F, and 28°C is about 82°F. You can approximate all the ones in between.

And -40°C is equal to -40°F. The two scales coincide at that temperature.

Forty is the only number that is spelt with its letters arranged in alphabetical order.

There is no Roman numeral for zero.

The numeral 4 is associated in Chinese culture with death. Many Chinese hospitals do not have a fourth floor.

Weird things that have been used as currencies:

Parmesan cheese (at the Credito Emiliano in Italy, cheese makers can use Parmesan as collateral for loans).

Salt (the word "salary" comes from the Latin word *salarium,* which in ancient Rome meant the amount of money given to a soldier to buy salt).

Tulips (in the Netherlands in the mid-1600s, tulips and their bulbs were used as money and were often left to relatives in people's wills. The rarest bulbs were worth several times the average person's annual income).

Cowry shells (once the most common form of currency throughout Asia and Africa, they were also used across Europe. Cowries are a form of sea snail – marine gastropods)

Whale teeth (used on the Fijian islands. In the 19th century, giving a whale tooth had the same significance as an engagement ring).

Potato mashers (once popular in the area of Africa that is now Cameroon).

Banknotes with holes in them (in 1997, the country then known as Zaire became the Democratic Republic of Congo following a coup, but all the banknotes carried the face of the former ruler. So people just cut out his picture and carried on using the notes).

In France a pie chart is often referred to as a Camembert.

The only Shakespeare play to contain the word "mathematics" is *The Taming of the Shrew*.

There are 43,252,003,274,489,856,000 ways to scramble a Rubik's Cube.

A circle has the largest area of any shape with the same perimeter. A circle also has the shortest perimeter of any shape with the same area.

Choose a four-digit number where all the digits are different. Arrange the digits of the four-digit number in descending, then ascending order. Subtract the smaller number from the bigger one. Repeat and repeat until you end up at 6174, which is known as Kaprekar's constant. If you then carry on repeating the process, you'll just keep on getting 6174 over and over again. Which would be boring, so stop as soon as you get to 6174.

Most people's favourite number is 7. Numerous polls have discovered 10% of those questioned choose it. The runner-up is 3.

There are 80,658,175,170,943,878,571,660,636,856,403,766, 975,289,505,440,883,277,824,000,000,000,000 ways to arrange a pack of cards. So, if you shuffle a deck properly, it's probable that exact order has never been seen before. Ever.

111,111,111 × 111,111,111 = 12,345,678,987,654,321

The average human produces anything up to 500 grams of poo a day. Although 75% of it is water, the average weight depends greatly on how much fibre you eat. Maths fans will be pleased to hear there's a formula for calculating poo weight. It's $Wf(1+Hf) + Wb(1+Hb) + Wm(1+Hm)$ where Wf, Wb and Wm are the weights of fibre, bacteria and metabolites in your colon, and Hf, Hb and Hm are the water-holding capacities of these substances. Who said maths was crap?

MYTH BUSTING

Myth: The biggest number is infinity.

Infinity is not a number, more a concept or idea, so it doesn't count (pun intended). A "googol" is the number 1 followed by 100 zeros (or 10^{100}). The biggest number commonly referred to with an actual name is a "googol-plex", which is the number 1 followed by a googol of zeros (or 10^{googol}). Mathematician Wolfgang H. Nitsche started trying to write it down in a series of books until it became clear he'd need 10,000,000,000,000,000,000,000,000,000,000 ,000,000,000,000,000,000,000,000,000,000,000,000,000, 000,000,000,000,000,000,000,000,000 volumes of the book to finish the number of zeros. Somebody else defined it as 1, followed by writing zeros until you got tired.

Even though a googolplex is huge, Skewes's and Graham's numbers are even larger. They are named after mathe-maticians Stanley Skewes and Ronald Graham. Both numbers are so big they can't be represented in the observable universe.

CHAPTER 7

LEAGUE OF NATIONS

No man is an island.

According to World Population Review, the most densely populated region in the world is the Chinese territory of Macau, with 19,737 people per square kilometre (ppsq/km).

However, Macau is not a separate nation, which means Monaco is the most densely populated independent country, with 19,361 ppsq/km.

These two are way ahead of third-placed Singapore on 8,019 (ppsq/km).

* * *

Greenland has the lowest population density in the world outside Antarctica, of 0.14 ppsq/km. Australia has a ppsq/

km ratio of 3, Canada 4, the United States 37, the United Kingdom 280.

New York City is sinking at the same rate as Venice – between 1 and 2 centimetres a year.

However, neither can match Mexico City, which in places is sinking at 50 centimetres a year. The Aztecs filled in Lake Texcoco to create an island and the Spanish colonisers built over the old Aztec city in the 1500s. The waters of the lake, however, are still used for the local water supply, meaning that as water is removed, the city sinks.

Mexico has the fewest public holidays of any major country: seven.

In Vietnam one in every four people has the surname Nguyen. In South Korea one in every five people has the surname Kim.

The most common surname in Australia, New Zealand, Canada, the United States, and the United Kingdom is Smith.

Gonzalez is the most common surname in Venezuela, Chile, Argentina, and Paraguay, but in Spain, it is Garcia.

The most common surname in the world is Wang, a surname shared by more than 107 million people. It is a

Mandarin term for king or prince. It is closely followed by Li (or Lee).

Nearly everybody (90% of the world's population) lives in the northern hemisphere.

The word "river" in some Scandinavian languages is Å, and both Norway and Sweden have villages called this. Sweden also has a village named Ö, which means "island", while France has a village called Y.

All the following have capital cities that were built, at least in part, especially for that purpose:

Australia (Canberra)

Barbados (Bridgetown)

Belize (Belmopan)

Brazil (Brasilia)

Federated States of Micronesia (Palikir)

India (New Delhi)

Ivory Coast (Yamoussoukro)

Kazakhstan (Astana)

Malaysia (Putrajaya)

Malta (Valetta)

Mauritania (Nouakchott)

Myanmar (Naypyidaw)

Nigeria (Abuja)

Pakistan (Islamabad)

Palau (Ngerulmud)

Peru (Lima)

South Africa (Pretoria)

Tanzania (Dodoma)

Turkey (Ankara)

United States (Washington DC)

The oldest of these is Lima (1535) and the most recent Ngerulmud (2006).

There are 44 landlocked countries in the world. The largest is Kazakhstan (2,724,900 square kilometres), the smallest is the Vatican City (0.44 square kilometres).

Italy contains two landlocked countries, the Vatican City and San Marino. The only other country completely landlocked within a single country is Lesotho, which is surrounded by South Africa.

Only two countries are "doubly landlocked" or surrounded by countries which are themselves landlocked. These are Uzbekistan (surrounded by the five landlocked countries of Afghanistan, Kazakhstan, Kyrgyzstan, Tajikistan, and

Turkmenistan) and Liechtenstein (surrounded by the landlocked countries of Switzerland and Austria).

The longest international border between two nations is that between Canada and the USA. It's 8891 kilometres long and takes in eight Canadian provinces and 13 US states. It is in two parts: Canada's border with the northern US states and a separate border it has with Alaska to the west.

Hungary and Finland are separated by 2200 kilometres and five countries (depending on which route you take) but their languages share around 200 words. Both languages come from the Uralic area of Asia and are known as Finno-Ugric languages. 10,000 years ago they shared the same language but today neither Finns nor Hungarians can understand each other.

Hungarian has 14 vowels: a, e, i, o, ö, u, ü, á, é, í, ó, ú, ő and ű.

The capital of Thailand, Bangkok's full name is Krung Thep Mahanakhon Amon Rattanakosin Mahinthara Yuthaya Mahadilok Phop Noppharat Ratchathani Burirom Udomratchaniwet Mahasathan Amon Piman Awatan Sathit Sakkathattiya Witsanukam Prasit.

There is a town in Oregon called Boring. Its motto is: "The most exciting place to live".

Dull is a village in Scotland, which is twinned with Boring, Oregon. Together with Bland, a town in Australia, they formed the League of Extraordinary Communities in 2013. They are more popularly known as the "Trinity of Tedium".

If every separatist movement in Europe was successful, the current map of 44 countries (give or take) would have to be redrawn to include more than 200 nations. The smallest might be Alderney in the Channel Islands, which would have a population of just over 2000.

In 1789, during the French Revolution, King Louis XVI and other aristocrats tried to escape. The revolutionary authorities then started demanding identification documents to exit or enter the country. This was possibly the first attempt to define a nation-state using the identity of its people rather than its monarchs' claims. "In 1789, almost nobody who lived in France thought of themselves as French. A hundred years later they all did," says John Breuilly, emeritus professor at the London School of Economics.

Passports as we know them were only introduced in the 1920s, when, after the First World War, the League of Nations (the forerunner of the United Nations) wanted to get a grip on the post-war refugee crisis, as the world was carved up by treaty into various blocs.

Before this official passport standard effectively became international law, some nations issued a "safe conduct pass" – a rather dramatic written plea that acted as a type of gentleman's agreement that a nation recognised another's territory and visiting it would not necessarily trigger a war. But essentially, before passports were introduced only a century ago, humans could wander pretty much anywhere they wished.

Russia has 11 time zones because of its huge east-west geographical span: 9000 kilometres. However, because France considers its overseas territories to be part of France itself, it is the country with the most time zones: 12.

Russia, the largest country in the world (17,125,192 square kilometres) also has the longest border of any nation: 57,792 kilometres.

Russia is only 3.8 kilometres from the United States at its nearest point. The Diomede Islands in the Bering Strait between Alaska and Siberia are divided between the two nations. Big Diomede belongs to Russia and Little Diomede to the US.

Big Diomede is almost a day ahead of Little Diomede, but not completely. Due to their locally defined time zones being linked to mainland USA and mainland Russia, Big Diomede is 21 hours ahead of Little Diomede in winter and 20 in summer. Because of this, the islands are sometimes called Tomorrow Island (Big Diomede) and Yesterday Island (Little Diomede).

MYTH BUSTING

Myth: The Great Wall of China is the only human-made object visible from space.

At around 6 metres wide, the wall cannot be viewed from outer space even if you take its shadow into account. The human eye could not make out such a narrow structure from outer space. It's the equivalent of seeing a hair from 3 kilometres away. It was one of the first things Neil Armstrong checked when he became the first man to walk on the Moon.

The collection of fortifications known as the Great Wall of China together span 21,196 kilometres, the longest feat of human engineering, and more than half the length of the equator. It was built over several centuries to protect imperial China from nomadic invaders from the Eurasian Steppe.

It's estimated that more than 400,000 prisoners and slave labourers died building the wall (almost half of the total workforce).

It's not a myth that rice is used as cement in the wall. Ground-up, glutinous rice flour mixed with water acts as mortar for the bricks and stones.

Quantity surveyors reckon there are approximately 3,873,000,000 bricks in the wall.

CHAPTER 8

SCIENCE AND SCIENTISTS

Humphry Davy makes
candle makers redundant.

Alessandro Volta (the clue is in the name) came up with the idea for the world's first battery in 1799 after he felt a tingling feeling when he put a silver spoon and a coin in his mouth. Quite why he did that no one knows. But he figured out that metals surrounded by brine could produce an electric charge. He was clearly an intrepid chap – after he built his first battery made of copper and zinc plates in brine, he decided to check it worked by placing the electrodes on his tongue. Ouch! It did. Three years later Humphry Davy would take Volta's work further by finding a use for the electric current batteries produced. However, his battery, made of metal plates immersed in acid, spluttered and splattered and stank so much that it was confined to the basement of the Royal Academy in London. But it had its uses. In the lecture theatre upstairs,

Davy showed how an electric current passing through a platinum strip generated a glow. He had created the world's first incandescent lamp and in 1809 went on to produce the first arc lamp. Holding an electrode in each (insulated) hand, he showed that, if they were moved close together, an electrical charge would arc between them through the air. Candle makers all over the planet groaned. In fact, they were probably incandescent . . .

*   *   *

In just one teaspoon of soil, there are more microorganisms than people on Earth.

You wouldn't have wanted to be James Phipps. In 1796 Phipps was the first recipient of a vaccine. And it was made from the contents of infected blisters. The inventor was physician Edward Jenner, who was attempting to find a way of stopping humans catching smallpox, one of the deadliest diseases in the 18th century. Jenner realised that milkmaids rarely caught smallpox, but that they did catch the related and less deadly disease of cowpox from the cows they milked. He figured that maybe there was something in cowpox that stopped them catching smallpox. So he scraped some of the goo from a pustule on a milkmaid's hands and injected it into young Phipps and then exposed the poor lad to smallpox. Medical ethics clearly differed notably in those days. Phipps remained immune and, from what today would almost certainly be deemed child abuse, came the world's first vaccine. It is estimated that Jenner has saved somewhere in the region of 600 million lives, possibly more than any other person in history.

The milkmaid with cowpox was called Sarah Nelmes and she caught the illness from her cow Blossom. Blossom's hide now hangs on the wall of St George's Medical School Library in Tooting, London.

The first anti-vaccination movements, backed by the church, who believed that smallpox was sent by God, began shortly after widespread smallpox vaccinations were introduced in the early 1800s.

There are eight times as many atoms in a teaspoon of water as there are teaspoonfuls of water in the Atlantic Ocean.

The periodic table, proposed by Russian chemist Dmitri Mendeleev in 1869, contains a list of all the elements currently known to humanity – a full 118. But chemists expect more to be discovered and so have already allocated a space for the 119th. Element 119 is hypothetical but it has a name (ununennium) and a chemical symbol (Uue) just waiting for it to be tracked down.

J is the only letter that doesn't appear on the periodic table.

Is a severed head briefly aware of what has happened to it? Well, where better to start than the French Revolution? French chemist Antoine Lavoisier faced beheading as an enemy of the state. He promised friends that, after Madame Guillotine lopped off his head, he would continue to blink for as long as he was conscious. And he did, apparently blinking for 15 seconds. This story has since been decried as apocryphal but the experiment was repeated by French physician Dr Gabriel Beaurieux, who, in 1905, asked condemned murderer Henri Languille to react if, following his decapitation, his name was called out. He shouted three times and, on the first two occasions, Languille lifted his eyelids. Thirty seconds after the guillotine had fallen, and on the third call, Languille's eyes stayed closed. Today physiologists believe that beheading causes momentary excruciating pain before, after about three seconds, consciousness is lost due to the sudden loss of blood pressure.

The last use of the guillotine in France was in 1977 in Baumettes prison in Marseilles, when Hamida Djandoubi, a Tunisian immigrant convicted of murder, was executed.

In 1927, the University of Queensland began an experiment to discover how slowly viscous substances such as pitch can move. So far, nine drops of pitch have dripped from the main body inside a funnel to the beaker below (the last was in 2014). It is the world's longest continuously running laboratory experiment.

After discovering the structure for deoxyribonucleic acid (or DNA), in 1953, Francis Crick and James Watson repaired to the Eagle pub in Cambridge, where they announced they'd "discovered the secret of life". The pub serves an Eagle's DNA beer to commemorate the occasion.

Humans share more than 60% of their DNA with bananas, about the same amount as we share with fruit flies.

The combined weight of humanity is about 350 million tonnes.

Hot water freezes faster than cold water. It's known as the Mpemba effect, after it was discovered in 1963 by a Tanzanian student Erasto Bartholomeo Mpemba, but it had been noted by Greek philosopher Aristotle, who described it as a "contrary quality" of water. The reason why is still not fully understood. Mpemba died in May, 2023.

Atoms are 99.999999999% empty space. So if you could squeeze all the empty space out of all the atoms in the world's 7.8 billion people, you could fit them into the volume of an ice cube. Enjoy that G&T.

Bananas and Brazil nuts are radioactive. Both contain potassium, and Brazil nuts contain a small amount of radium from the soil they grow in. Both potassium and radium break down and emit radiation but the amounts are tiny. The United States Environmental Protection Agency describes both foods as harmless and beneficial to human health. You'd need to eat 10 million bananas all at once to die of radiation sickness.

The US National Academy of Science's Institute of Medicine estimates that around 7000 people die in the US every year because of incomprehensible writing on doctors' notes.

Approximately 150,000 people die every day worldwide.

MYTH BUSTING

Myth: Malaria has killed more than half of everyone who ever lived.

Malaria is a big killer, that's for sure. But for it to have killed half of all humans who have died, it would have bumped off about 54 billion people. Not only that, but the annual death toll from malaria today is around 1%. Yes, we have drugs to prevent it that didn't exist before but, even during the 19th century, when malaria was far more prevalent and deadly, only 1 person in 10 who caught it would die from it. The true historical death toll from malaria is, therefore, according to Brian Gallagher, Emeritus Professor of Medical Statistics at Liverpool School of Tropical Medicine, more likely to be around 5% than 50%.

Myth: Women are just as good as men at throwing.

Sadly, this appears not to be true. Professor Linda Duffy, a former number one world darts player who became a sports scientist at Middlesex University, has studied throwing by boys, girls, men, and women, and has discovered that whatever the age, males are always more accurate. "It doesn't matter what task you give them – balls, bags, beanbags, darts – men are always better at hitting the target," says Duffy. "I still haven't figured out the reason, although research is ongoing."

Myth: The water flows down the plughole in a different direction depending on which hemisphere you are in.

It's a myth, but only partially. The story goes that, because of the Coriolis force created by the Earth's rotation, and this differs on either side of the equator, the water will swirl down your bath's plughole – anticlockwise in the northern hemisphere, clockwise in the southern. While it's true the Coriolis force does act on the winds or hurricanes in our atmosphere or currents in the ocean, it has little effect on your bath. Your tub shape, tap position, or the swirl of water currents as it is filling, or indeed the water temperature, have a far greater effect. You can even make the water swirl the opposite way by swishing it with your hand. However, if you let your water stand in a room with no draughts or sunlight (for heat) for three days, as some Australian and American physicists (in different hemispheres) did in the 1960s, then maybe you'll see the Coriolis force at work. But you'll need a big tub. The researchers used ones that were totally spherical and two metres in diameter. And you need to be able to remove the plug from the outside so you don't disturb the water. Sure enough, the researchers reported the water spinning in opposite ways as it drained.

Some Australian toilet manufacturers have taken to selling backward-spinning dunnies to cash in on the phenomenon. Who knows if they design them so that they always spin the right (or wrong) way?

CHAPTER 9

OCEAN DEEP, MOUNTAIN HIGH

This is Planet Earth.

The biggest earthquake ever recorded was the Great Chilean Earthquake of 22 May, 1960. It measured 9.5 out of 10 on the moment magnitude scale, which has replaced the Richter scale. The ground shifted 30 metres in places close to the epicentre at Lumaco.

The deadliest earthquake occurred in Shaanxi province in China in 1556 – 100,000 people are believed to have been killed immediately with another 730,000 dying of famine or illness in the months afterwards.

By comparison, the eruption of Etna in the year 79, which buried the city of Pompeii and villages in the surrounding region, killed around 16,000 people. Most of them died of asphyxiation from the gases and ash filling the air rather than being buried beneath volcanic debris.

The sound made by Krakatoa when the Indonesian volcano erupted in 1883 ruptured the eardrums of people 65 kilometres away. The sound wave travelled around the Earth four times.

* * *

The Bay of Fundy on Canada's east coast is where the largest tidal variation in the world occurs. The difference between low and high tide can be as much as 16 metres. The average tidal range for the rest of the world is only about one metre.

The only opening between the Mediterranean Sea and the Atlantic Ocean is at the Straits of Gibraltar, 24 kilometres wide at its narrowest. Without the Atlantic connection the Mediterranean would dry up, meaning that a million cubic metres of water flow through the Straits every second.

The Earth's magnetic field flips. North becomes south and vice versa. The reversals are random, with no apparent timescale or frequency to their occurrence. They can happen as often as every 10,000 years or so and as infrequently as every 50,000,000 years. The last reversal was about 780,000 years ago. It isn't an instantaneous process and takes place over hundreds or thousands of years.

The Earth's magnetic north pole has been creeping northward – 1100 kilometres – since the early 19th century, when explorers first located it. It is currently migrating northward about 65 kilometres per year, as opposed to about 17 kilometres per year in the early 20th century.

The coldest place on Earth is Antarctica, where a record low of –89.2°C was recorded on 21 July, 1983.

Antarctica is also the driest continent on Earth, with an average annual rain-/snowfall of around 5 centimetres.

It is colder at the South Pole, an average of –60°C in winter, than at the North Pole, average –30°C. There are numerous reasons but the main one is that the South Pole – on land and in a mountainous region – is much higher. It's around 2800 metres above sea level, whereas the North Pole sits on the ice at sea level.

Everywhere on Earth, from the poles to the equator, receives the same amount of daylight in a year (or it would if the Earth were a smooth sphere with no mountains and valleys creating shade).

Although we are wise to be concerned about deforestation, trees still cover a third of the planet's land surface. As much as 45% of the carbon stored on land is tied up in forests.

Only about 2.5% of the Earth's water is fresh water. Of that, only about a third is drinkable.

In the Philippines is Vulcan Point, an extinct volcano that forms an island within Main Crater Lake. This lake is found on Volcano Island which is located in the middle of Lake Taal. Lake Taal is on the island of Luzon. All of which means there is an island in a lake on an island in a lake on an island.

It's not the only place where this configuration occurs. Visit Victoria Island in Canada to see a similar geographical anomaly.

The Philippines is made up of 7641 islands (until 2017 geographers had thought it only contained 7107).

The deepest part of any ocean is the Challenger Deep, part of the Mariana Trench in the northwest Pacific. Measurements have put its depth at anywhere between 10,911 and 11,034 metres. The pressure of the water there is 12,600 per square metre, or around 1100 times that at sea level. No light can penetrate such a depth and the water is only one degree above freezing. No fish can survive but nonetheless other animal life can exist there, including a large amoeba called foraminifera, shrimplike amphipods, and sea cucumbers.

The first people to travel to the bottom of Challenger Deep were Jacques Piccard, a Swiss oceanographer, and

Don Welsh, a US Navy lieutenant, on 23 January, 1960. It took them five hours. Their submersible, a bathyscaph called *Trieste*, had steel walls 13 centimetres thick. The window cracked and leaked, but they got to the bottom. It was 2012 before anyone visited again.

Iceland gets wider by, on average, five centimetres a year because it is situated on the Mid-Atlantic Ridge, where two of the Earth's tectonic plates are moving apart,

On the other side of America, tectonic plates are moving towards each other, meaning the Pacific Ocean gets narrower by about 3 centimetres a year.

The continents shift, on average, at about the same rate as your fingernails grow.

However, the Australian tectonic plate is moving so quickly that Global Positioning Systems are 1.8 metres out from where they were when they were last adjusted in 1994.

Canada's coastline is the longest in the world, measuring 243,042 kilometres, including the mainland coast and its offshore islands.

Canada is also home to 31,752 lakes larger than three square kilometres.

The Earth isn't a perfect sphere. It bulges at the equator and is flattened at the poles because of the force of its rotation and because it's not solid on the inside. The diameter at the poles is about 12,714 kilometres and at the equator is about 12,756 kilometres. Keep reading to find out why this might disappoint anyone who has climbed Mount Everest.

The greatest sheer vertical drop is found on Mount Thor on Baffin Island in Canada. Fall off and you won't hit the bottom for 1250 metres, 16 seconds later.

The Dead Sea is 430 metres below sea level, and sinking.

Australia is wider than the Moon.

Point Nemo, in the Pacific Ocean, is the most remote place on Earth, about 2688 kilometres from the nearest land – Ducie Island, part of the Pitcairn Islands, to the north; Motu Nui, one of the Easter Islands, to the northeast; and Maher Island, part of Antarctica, to the south. When the astronauts aboard the International Space Station pass overhead, they are usually the nearest humans to Point Nemo.

MYTH BUSTING

Myth: Everest is the tallest mountain on Earth.

No, it isn't. Manua Kea in Hawaii is, but most of it is under water. While its base is difficult to determine, organisations such as the US Geological Survey accept that Manua Kea is 10,210 metres tall. Everest is a mere 8849.

The summit of Everest is, however, the highest point above sea level.

It's not the closest point on Earth to outer space, though, nor the furthest point from the Earth's centre. And that's because the Earth isn't a sphere (see earlier in this chapter). Ecuador's Mount Chimborazo is about 2600 metres shorter than Everest but, because it is situated close to the Earth's bulging equator, it is closer to space.

Everest is estimated to weigh about 161,932,476,090 tonnes.

The death rate among people attempting to climb Everest is about one in 100. But the number of deaths per successful ascent is about four in 100. The death rate is falling, however. The 1970s were the deadliest decade, when the death rate per 100 climbers reached almost 2.2.

The most common form of death on Everest is suffocation by avalanche.

Two men recently held the record for the most ascents of Everest: 26 each. Pasang Dawa Sherpa equalled Kami Rita Sherpa's record when he reached the summit on 14 May, 2023. But then Rita went and climbed it again on 17 May. So on 22 May Dawa went up once more to re-equal the record of 27 climbs. It lasted one day. On 23 May, Rita topped Everest again, leaving him alone on 28 summits. Currently.

By far the deadliest mountain in the Himalayas is Annapurna. For decades it held the highest fatality-to-successful climbs rate, at around 32%. However, in recent years the rate has fallen and recent figures show that it is now at 22%, just under the 24% estimate for K2 on the Pakistan-China border.

Myth: Quicksand sucks you under.

We've all seen the B-movies. Baddie trying to escape from the law blunders his way into quicksand. He gets sucked deeper and deeper as he struggles, until all that is left is his outstretched, desperate hand or his floating cowboy hat. Doubtless he deserved everything he got, the nasty piece of work, but is it true? Was he really sucked under the surface? Quicksand is usually a mixture of water-logged sand or clay, often near a tidal river. And when you step on it, you sink into it a bit. But experiments have proved you never sink deep enough to drown and, crucially, you are not being sucked in, it's the pressure caused by your weight that pushes you in. Yet it's never far enough to overwhelm you, because humans are more buoyant than quicksand. That said, quicksand can trap you long enough for the tide to sweep in and drown you. So give it a wide berth if you see it. But if you don't . . .

The best way to escape quicksand is not to struggle (possibly easier said than done). Wiggle a leg gently, which introduces more water into the sand around it making it easier to move, and then start wading slowly towards the edge. You can also float on quicksand and swim ever so slowly to the edge, but be sure to lie on your back so your nose protrudes, not your front.

CHAPTER 10

DRINK

Shaken, not stirred.

If you only know one thing about vodka martinis, you'll know that's how James Bond, the world's most famous fictional spy, drinks them. But martini aficionados insist that the cocktail should be stirred, never shaken. Did one of the most fabled bons vivants get it all wrong?

Brian Silva, legendary bartender at Rules, London's oldest restaurant, says, "If you shake them the ice breaks up, melts, and you can't control the dilution, which is key to the perfect martini." Yet, like 007 himself, James Bond's creator Ian Fleming was an epicurean, who drank martinis in some of the world's most famous bars. He would surely have known this. So why did his most famous character go awry? Well he didn't, of course. And the clues are in Fleming's books, which were written shortly after the end of the Second World War. Back then, grain that in peacetime would have been used to distil vodka was desperately needed to make bread for impoverished populations across Europe. But, of course, people still liked boozing, and so started distilling, using anything they could, quite often root vegetables well past their prime.

Unsurprisingly, these vodkas didn't match up to the previous grain-made versions, often displaying an oily mouth feel, caused by the presence of fusel oil, a by-product of poor production. *Fusel* translates as "bad liquor" in German. In the novel *Moonraker*, Bond drops a few peppercorns into his vodka. This was a common trick to counteract the fusel oil, while, in *Casino Royale*, Bond remarks that his martini would be better if the vodka was made with grain. Even more crucially, if non-grain vodkas are shaken with ice, the oiliness dissipates notably. Fleming knew full well why vodka martinis in that era should be shaken and not stirred. So, it seems that Bond and Fleming were living up to their reputations as gourmands after all. How could we have doubted them?

Since this author first dissected Bond's boozing habits, we have learnt more about root-veg vodkas. Parsnips can suffer from root canker, which is caused by a fungus attacking the plant. Nonetheless, vodka makers still used them despite the mould-like flavour they add to the drink. Bond had another trick up his sleeve. Choosing a lemon twist rather than an olive garnish for his martini adds citric acid to the mix, which counteracts the off flavour.

And there's more. It seems beetroot contains phytosterols, which can reduce cholesterol. Because old beetroots were used in some post-war vodkas, Bond was also knocking back the martinis to preserve his health. Well, maybe.

Even though dry vermouth is used to make a martini, the "dryness" of a martini refers to how much spirit (gin or vodka) is used, not how much vermouth. If you want a dry martini, you are asking for a higher proportion of spirit. A naked martini is one where vermouth is no more than one drop, if that.

It's said that Winston Churchill liked his martinis so dry that he merely glanced at the bottle of vermouth on the shelf before pouring himself a large measure of gin.

Was Charles Dickens a martini fan? The traditional garnish for a martini is a lemon twist or olives. Why else would Dickens name one of his novels *Olive or Twist*?

* * *

The most common pub name in England is The Red Lion. A red lion was the personal crest of John of Gaunt, the third son of Edward III.

Spain has more bars serving alcohol per citizen than any other European Union country.

Gin and rum are known as Navy Strength if their alcohol content is more than 57.15%. This is because when they were carried in wooden barrels on the ships of the Royal Navy, sometimes the barrels would get damaged and leak their contents onto the gunpowder used for the ships' cannons. If the alcohol was below 57.15%, the gunpowder would no longer ignite and was useless.

This is also where the term "proof" comes from when used to indicate the strength of an alcohol. If the gunpowder would still burn after being soaked in the alcohol, the gin or rum was declared "gunpowder-proof" and allowed on board.

However, other historians say that the officers on naval ships wanted "proof" that they weren't being fobbed off with weak alcohol and so they mixed a small amount of gin with gunpowder and, if it still ignited, that was proof they had a decent strength gin.

The rum ration (a tot of 71 millilitres but, in centuries past, half a pint) given daily to all sailors in the Royal Navy was only abolished in 1970. Teetotal sailors could opt for the monetary value of the drink instead. Prior to the Napoleonic Wars, a Royal Navy sailor's daily alcohol ration was a gallon of beer. Yes, that's eight pints, or 4.5 litres a day!

Is there a double malt whisky? Yes. Single malt whiskies are the product of a single distillery aged for at least three years, whereas a double malt is a blend of two single malts to produce a specific taste. This differs from a normal blend, which can contain numerous different whiskies. So double malt whiskies exist, but does Single Gloucester cheese? Find out on page 44.

Germans call lager "Pilsner" (from Pilsen, the German name for Plzeň) because the first lager came from Plzeň in the Czech Republic. Pilsner Urquell, or "pilsner from the original source", was first brewed in 1842 and still exists.

Just down the road from Pilsen is the town of České Budějovice, or Budweis in German. It gave its name to Budweiser lager, first brewed in 1802. But later that century Adolphus Busch in the US also began brewing a beer called Budweiser. This didn't matter so much until the globalisation of trade meant the two began to be sold side by side, which confused drinkers. The compromise, which has made a few thousand lawyers very rich, is for the American version to change its name to Bud in some countries or the Czech version to change its name to Budvar or Czechvar in others. Today, only in Britain are the two beers permitted to use their full names.

American Budweiser is often regarded as the world's best-selling beer. But actually it's just the most ubiquitous. And it's only because most people have never heard of Snow. Snow is only sold in China but tops the world's bestseller list with 101 million hectolitres sold each year.

Lager is called "lager" in the English-speaking world because *Lager* means "cellar or store" in German. And lager needs to lager in a *Lager* before it can be drunk.

Coca-Cola really did once contain cocaine. It is made from the coca plant, from which cocaine comes, and shortly after the drink was invented in 1886, it contained traces of the drug (which wasn't illegal back then). Today it contains a "non-narcotic extract" of the coca plant.

The recipe for Coca-Cola is kept under lock and key in a vault at the World of Coca-Cola Museum in Atlanta, Georgia. In 2007 former Coca-Cola employee Joya Williams was jailed for eight years for trying to sell company secrets to rival cola maker Pepsi who dobbed her in.

Coca-Cola is so popular in Mexico that the St John the Baptist Church in San Juan Chamula offers its members the drink so they can burp out the evil spirits infecting their souls.

Crossing your arms while drinking a toast is considered rude in the Czech Republic.

Clinking glasses while toasting is considered a no-go in Hungary. The ritual is associated with the Austrian generals who executed Hungarian rebels during the years of the Austro-Hungarian Empire.

The longest word for "cheers" is the Tamil Nallārōkkiyam peruka, although in terms of complex pronunciation, Hungary's *Egészségére* runs it close.

Baby mice wine is made of day-old baby mice, drowned in rice wine and left to ferment for up to 14 months. It is drunk in China for its healing properties.

The Sourtoe is the signature cocktail served in a bar in Yukon, Canada. It contains the mummified toe of an illegal bootlegger called Louie Linken, who lost it to frostbite in the 1920s. His brother Otto preserved it in alcohol and it became the Sourtoe Cocktail in 1973. Whenever someone swallows the toe, it is replaced by another.

Kopi luwak, or cat poo coffee, is a speciality in Indonesia. Cats are fed on coffee beans and their poo collected to make the coffee. It seems it tastes smoother. But if you are crazy enough to want to try it, make sure it comes from free-range cats. The industry is noted for its cruelty to the animals (you can also try panda dung tea in China, although it costs about US $150 a cup).

Cow urine is popular neat in some parts of India. Some Hindu spiritual leaders say it wards off illness.

Tuna eye lenses, are, for some reason, popular in South Korea. They are added to rice wine and make it taste fishy. Unsurprisingly. They are also supposed to have anti-ageing properties.

If you drink tea with milk in it, do you add the milk before the tea or after? Well, whatever way you do it, it will be a pointer to your position in society. Many years ago, low-quality china cups owned by poorer people would crack when hot tea was poured into them. But if they put cold milk in first that protected the cups. However, high-quality china could withstand hot tea, so putting milk in last was a pointed way of showing you were wealthy enough to have fine china on your table.

Smurf, a cow living on a farm on Ontario in Canada, holds the record for the greatest yield of milk in a bovine lifetime. Up to February 2012, when she was 15 years old, she produced 216,891 litres of milk. At that rate it would take Smurf 1 trillion years to fill the Grand Canyon with milk. By which time it would have curdled very badly.

An ancient Russian tradition believed that putting a frog into a pail of milk kept it fresh. They may have been correct. Researchers in Moscow, Stockholm and Kuopio in Finland identified almost 100 substances secreted from the skin of the Russian brown frog that have antimicrobial properties capable of attacking the likes of *Salmonella* and *Staphylococcus* bacteria.

Cleopatra, ancient queen of Egypt, bathed in donkey milk to keep her skin wrinkle-free. She may have been on to something. When milk sours, its sugar – lactose – is converted by bacteria into lactic acid, which, when applied to skin, causes the surface layer to peel off and reveal blemish-free skin beneath. For what it's worth, she also used powdered crocodile poo to enhance her complexion.

According to the US Institutes of Health, 68% of the world's population is lactose-intolerant (we'll have to hope Cleopatra was one of the 32% who wasn't), ranging from about 5% of northern Europeans to about 90% of adults in some parts of Asia.

MYTH BUSTING

Myth: mixing your drinks gets you more drunk.

No, it doesn't. Your level of drunkenness is purely a matter of how much alcohol you consume. However, there is evidence to suggest that mixing drinks can make it more difficult to calculate how much alcohol you have consumed, thus muddying the waters (as well as your brain). And there is another strand of thought that suggests fizzy drinks get you drunker more quickly because the bubbles increase the pressure in your stomach, forcing alcohol into your bloodstream more quickly.

Even more evidence suggests that darker drinks, such as red wine and whisky, will lead to a worse hangover (not that I am suggesting anything should be consumed to excess). It's not noted how many people volunteered but studies carried out by the National Center for Biotechnology Information in the US found that worse hangovers were suffered by test subjects who drank (dark) bourbon than by those who drank (clear) vodka. This is because dark alcoholic drinks contain compounds known as congeners, minor compounds other than ethanol that occur naturally in alcoholic beverages as a result of distilling and fermenting processes. One of these compounds is methanol, which is metabolised by our bodies into formaldehyde, a toxic substance that in large quantities can cause blindness or death. No wonder your head is ringing. As I said before, nothing to excess.

The UK government advises drinkers of both sexes to consume no more than 14 units of alcohol a week. But the guidance from other governments varies widely, as does what constitutes a single unit. I've attempted to match the levels given below to the UK standard unit of 8 grams of pure alcohol:

Spain 35 units for men, 21 for women

France 28 units for men, 17.5 for women

US 24 units for men, 12 for women

Italy 23 units for men, 15 for women

Ireland 21 for men, 14 for women

Australia 17.5 units for both

Hong Kong has no safe limit

It seems like the lesson here is if you want to drink and feel less guilty, move to Hong Kong. Or Spain. Or actually, the Basque Country. For whatever reason, Basques are allowed to drink more than their compatriots, according to their own regional guidelines. And that's a whopping 61 units for both men and women. Topa!

Myth: Coffee cures hangovers.

All coffee does is reduce the fatigue you may be feeling through the stimulant effect of the caffeine, according to the Center of Alcohol Studies at Rutgers University in New Jersey. In some cases, it may make the hangover worse by inducing headaches and irritating your stomach lining.

Other hangover cures that the research centre dismisses include "the hair of the dog" or having another alcoholic drink to counteract the hangover. It has a sedative effect, they say, but when it wears off you need another, stronger drink. So quit while you are ahead (if somewhat groggy). They also insist a big, greasy breakfast won't help. It takes your mind off your throbbing head but is hard to digest, making your body work even harder to dispel your hangover.

However, the centre says that a calorie-laden meal before drinking does have a positive effect, slowing down the absorption of alcohol. Drink water alongside your alcohol and again before going to sleep. And if that doesn't work and you still have a hangover, they recommend consuming sports drinks with electrolytes, which are lost from your body due to the diuretic effect of alcohol.

If all else fails, perhaps we should turn to the people of Puerto Rico who rub half a lemon under their drinking arm to ward off hangovers.

CHAPTER 11

PLANES, TRAINS AND AUTOMOBILES

Don't drive my car.

According to an estimate by the World Health Organization, cars may be the deadliest human invention, surpassing numerous weapons intended for that purpose. The WHO estimates that 1.2 million people a year die in road traffic accidents and an additional 1.2 million die from pollution caused by cars. There are also the people who die from environmental changes caused by climate change. Currently, this total is much higher than the annual number of people directly killed by war, somewhere between 100,000 and 200,000. That said, deaths from automobile accidents were historically fewer, and deaths from war, historically greater than they are today.

* * *

The crew of Apollo 10 travelled faster than any humans anywhere before or since when, on 26 May, 1969, their spacecraft reached 39,937.7 kilometres per hour. US astronauts Thomas Stafford, Eugene Cernan, and John Young were returning from the dress rehearsal for the first Moon landing, which would take place two months later.

The first world land speed record was set in 1898 when Gaston de Chasseloup-Laubat set a speed of 63.15 kilometres per hour at Achères, France, driving his Jeantaud Duc. Currently it is held by Briton Andy Street, who in 1997 drove his ThrustSSC at 1227.968 kph at Black Rock Desert in the US. This is faster than the speed of sound and ThrustSSC created a sonic boom as it crossed the timing line.

The Le Mans 24-hour race is often described as motor sport's most arduous challenge. And only one driver has ever successfully completed the entire race by himself, a practice now outlawed as too dangerous. He was Edward Ramsden Hall, the son of a wealthy mill owner from Huddersfield in West Yorkshire, who in 1950 managed to drive the full 24 hours with no team-mate sharing the driving stints. He finished eighth. When asked how, he answered, "By wearing green overalls, dear boy." Two other drivers came close to achieving the same feat, one of them winning and the other coming agonisingly close. In 1950 French driver Louis Rosier planned to drive the entire race alone. However, unlike Ramsden Hall, he drew the line at defecating in his racing overalls. With only two hours left to run, he stopped for a comfort break, handing his car over to his son and co-driver, who drove two laps. They did, however, go on to win. And in 1952 Pierre Levegh was leading the race with only 50 minutes remaining after an epic solo drive when tiredness meant he missed a gear change and broke his car's crankshaft.

Pierre Levegh is now remembered for something other than his solo drive in 1952. Two and half hours into the 1955 Le Mans 24 Hours, his Mercedes struck the back of Lance Macklin's Austin Healey opposite the main grand-stand and ploughed into the crowd – 83 spectators plus Levegh were killed. A priest who attended the dead and dying said, "I now know what hell looks like." It was the worst accident in motor-racing history.

In 1988 Roger Dorchy hit a record speed of 407 kilometres per hour on Le Mans's long Mulsanne straight. He was driving a car designed by Peugeot engineers. Because Peugeot were about to launch their new road car, the 405, the company insisted that Dorchy's speed was 2 kph slower than it really was, meaning that the official record is 405 kph. (Nobody seems to have asked Dorchy if he was miffed.)

The Isle of Man TT motorcycle races are even more dangerous than Le Mans once was. In the event's 116-year history, 266 riders have died. Six riders died in 2022, equalling the worst record for a single year and in only one year out of the last 85 has nobody died.

Amsterdam airport Schiphol is four metres below sea level.

El Alto in La Paz, Bolivia, is the highest international airport at 4062 metres above sea level. It is a myth that aircraft landing there have to depressurise their cabins because the doors would blow off if they didn't. However, they do reduce the cabin pressure to below standard levels so that passengers can acclimatise to the lower pressure in the city and this also reduces airsickness.

Airliners used to have a separate navigator in the cockpit in addition to the captain and first officer, in some cases still using stars and ground landmarks to direct the aircraft. As sophisticated electronic navigation systems, and then satellite positioning systems, were introduced, most civilian air navigators were made redundant by the early 1980s.

The Mallard set a record speed for a steam locomotive of 126 miles per hour (203 kilometres per hour) on the UK's East Coast Main Line in 1938, a figure that remains unmatched.

Cleckheaton Central station in West Yorkshire is the only railway station in the world to have been stolen. The station had closed in 1965 but parts of it remained in situ. In 1971 a contractor was employed to clear the site but, when he arrived, he discovered there was nothing to remove. The following year a man was convicted of stealing stone, timber, metal, track, chairs and even the buffers from the site. The prosecution counsel pronounced that "this man last August, in effect, stole Cleckheaton station".

The world's oldest underground railway, metro, or subway is London's, which opened in 1863.

Some fans of the Budapest Metro says that theirs is older (it was opened in 1896) because the London Underground was, at first, a normal steam railway that just happened to run through tunnels, whereas Budapest's was a purpose-built underground electric railway right from the start. Budapest's is the only metro system deemed a UNESCO World Heritage Site.

The world's longest metro is the Shanghai Metro at 802 kilometres. However, the New York City Subway has more stations: 472.

The world's shortest metro system is the 3.8-kilometre Metropolitana di Catania on Sicily which consists of one line and six stations.

The deepest metro station in the world is Arsenalna station on the Kiev Metro at 107 metres deep, although some tunnels on the Pyongyang Metro are 110 metres deep.

Russia's Trans-Siberian Railway crosses 3901 bridges.

British Army tanks have tea-making facilities.

London's black-cab drivers must pass "The Knowledge" before being allowed to operate. The test, considered the toughest in the world, involves learning the whereabouts of 25,000 streets and 20,000 landmarks.

Commercial jet aircraft are struck by lightning at least once a year.

The first person to reach the South Pole, located pretty much in the centre of the Antarctic continent, was Norwegian explorer Roald Amundsen, who arrived on 14 December, 1911, beating British Royal Navy Captain Robert Scott by 33 days. Scott and his party, of course, died on the return trek, a mere 17 kilometres from their next supply depot, after a journey on foot of more than 2500 kilometres.

Amundsen and Scott had a rival. A third man was attempting to get to the South Pole at the same time. Nobu Shirase was a Japanese explorer widely ridiculed back home – nobody could see the point – but he managed to travel to within 1100 kilometres of the pole, using bamboo sleds pulled by dogs.

Nobu Shirase was born in 1861. The law in Japan at that time forbade any person to leave the country. Any attempt was punishable by death. The law was rescinded when the ruling Tokugawa shogunate was overthrown in 1868, which was rather fortunate for the budding explorer.

While Roald Amundsen was undoubtedly the first human to reach the South Pole, there is dispute over who was the first to reach the North Pole, not least because there is no actual land there. Unlike the South Pole, which is a fixed point on a continental land mass, the fixed point of the North Pole is on the seabed, beneath a constantly shifting body of sea ice. When in the early years of the 20th century explorers were attempting to win the race to get to the pole, not only was the ground beneath their feet shifting, but their instrumentation was not as accurate as it is today. The first claim was made by American Frederick Cook, alongside two Inuit men, Ahwelah and Etukishook, on 21 April, 1908. But it was disputed by former colleagues of Cook, who accused him of lying about his earlier mountain-climbing exploits. Not only that, but Cook claimed the records of his journey to the pole had been "left behind" in Greenland. Next up was another American, Robert Peary. Peary was an irascible man described by Fergus Fleming, author of *Ninety Degrees North: The Quest for the North Pole*, as "the most unpleasant man in the annals of polar exploration". True or otherwise, Peary claimed he had reached the pole, alongside companion Matthew Henson, and four Inuit men Ootah, Seeglo, Ooqueah and Egingwah, on 6 April 1909. Except that, if he did, Henson got there just before him and, not wanting to upset Peary, waited before saying he believed they had arrived at the pole. Peary, apparently, would not have been happy because Henson was an African-American and Peary was white and wanted the glory. But it seems maybe neither got there. Peary's records simply did not tally, he had no navigational training, and his log books were only updated with slips of paper on his return. Considering the slapdash, duplicitous approach of both Cook and Peary, perhaps the only satisfactory outcome is that neither of them got there first.

So who did? Well, the first fully verified visitor was American high-school dropout and snowmobile enthusiast Ralph Plaisted, who buzzed his way there on 19 April, 1968. Yes, a full six decades after Cook! But riding a snowmobile was outside the spirit of the rules, said the sticklers at the *Guinness Book of Records*, he might as well have flown there. Instead the honour eventually fell to Briton Wally Herbert, who got to the pole one year later on 6 April, 1969, making small patriotic amends for Scott's failure all those years earlier.

MYTH BUSTING

Myth: The Wright brothers invented, built and flew the world's first powered aeroplane.

Strictly speaking, they most certainly did. But in the summer of 1853, 50 years before the Wrights flew at Kitty Hawk in North Carolina, another crewed flight took place.

Sir George Cayley, a member of the British parliament, landowner, and amateur scientist, proved his theory of aerodynamics by flying his coachman in a kite-shaped glider across the grounds of Brompton Hall, in Yorkshire, using the same aerodynamics the Wright brothers used. It vindicated Cayley's belief that air passing over a curved wing generated lift. "Had there been a suitable engine available to power it, then the world might well not be celebrating the Wrights' centenary, but Cayley's 150th," Ian Wormald, a retired squadron leader and former British Aerospace test pilot, told *The Independent* in 2003.

Myth: If the V2 had been built earlier, Germany would have won the Second World War.

In 1944 Nazi Germany invented the world's first ballistic missile. It was a huge military and technological advance. V2s were frightening, you couldn't hear them coming because they travelled faster than the speed of sound, and they left very large holes where they landed, but their destructive capacity was limited. "It's one of the great wartime myths," says Mike Neufeld of Washington DC's Air and Space Museum, and the world's expert on the rocket. "V2s were a great psychological weapon, but they had only a fraction of the destructive force of a fully laden bomber aircraft. It's simply not true that they could have won the war. Yet the fallacy exists to this day."

Myth: Submarines blast out air so they can dive beneath the water.

Another spectacular effect beloved of Hollywood film directors is a fast-submerging submarine venting vast amounts of air to allow it to sink. The bubbles might look spectacular, but that would be a waste of the air the submarine needs. Instead, submarines have ballast tanks that can be filled with air or water. On the surface these are filled with air. When the submarine is preparing to submerge, vents underneath the submarine are opened, allowing seawater to flood upwards into the tanks and pushing out the air that was there before. To surface, a submarine will not usually fill these tanks with air while still submerged. Instead it will head to the surface using only its hydroplanes and propulsion system and, when just beneath the surface, raise its snorkel and begin filling its ballast tanks with air. This does, however, take longer than the dive sequence so, if a rare emergency occurs and the submarine needs to surface quickly, emergency compressed air tanks are called into action.

At this point you might be asking yourself how come the compressed air that submarines carry for emergencies doesn't make them float. Try this experiment. Get hold of one of those sachets of ketchup or mayonnaise that pubs stock. Fill a 2-litre plastic drinks bottle with water. Pop the sachet into the bottle – it should float. Screw the bottle top on tightly and squeeze the bottle hard. The sachet will sink. Release the pressure and it will rise.

Practise your squeeze for long enough and you can position the sachet halfway down the bottle. This is because when you squeeze the bottle, the tiny gas bubble in the sachet that is making it float is compressed, it shrinks in size, and the sachet sinks. This is why a submarine's compressed air supply doesn't make the submarine buoyant.

Submarine films also often show two rival submarines in close quarters deep in the ocean. Neither side wishes to be detected so their captains order "silent running", which means the crew should not make any excess noise, including speaking. But could somebody talking on a submarine really be heard on another nearby? Yes, they could. Especially if they were touching a part of the boat that leads to the outside hull. Even worse would be a dropped tool. Noise is passed through solids and liquids far more easily than it passed through the air. In the ocean, everyone can hear you scream . . .

Sound travels about four times faster in water than in air.

Myth: When you are booking a train or plane journey online and are told "Last two seats at this price", it's a ploy to make you buy.

Not according to Airlines for America, the association for airlines based in the US. There really are only two, it insists. Try buying three and you'll see for yourself.

Myth: You are already dead from a heart attack before you hit the ground after a fall from a great height.

Not so. In 1972, Serbian flight attendant Vesna Vulović fell from her aeroplane 10,160 metres above Czechoslovakia after terrorists exploded a bomb in its baggage compartment. She was the only survivor. Her astonishing fortune was attributed to the fact that she was pinned to a part of the broken fuselage by her food service trolley and this landed in a snow-covered forest, which cushioned the impact. Her doctors also noted she had low blood pressure, meaning that when the plane broke apart in the low pressure at high altitude, her heart wasn't put under great strain. It is the highest fall from which anybody has survived without a parachute. She had no recollection of the incident, which is probably all for the best.

Myth: The protective brace position you are told to adopt on aircraft is merely so your teeth are preserved in the event of a fatal crash, so helping accident investigators identify who you are.

The brace position involves putting knees and feet together, placing your arms over your head, and leaning forward into the seat in front of you. But how can this protect you? Some sceptics have even suggested it is designed to deliberately kill you by breaking your neck, thus ensuring you die quickly rather than from painful injuries. Neither myth is true. Adopting the brace position saves lives. It is designed to minimise the impact of the crash on your body, protecting your head and arms, and stopping your body from jack-knifing and your shins from hitting the seat in front of you. Studies of aircraft accidents, including the 1989 Kegworth crash in the UK, show that there were fewer deaths among those passengers who adopted the brace position. Tests on crash dummies have show the same outcomes, while the lack of fatalities aboard the US Airways flight that came down on New York's Hudson River in 2009 has been attributed to adopting the brace position. So when the cabin crew shout, "Brace, brace!", you'd better brace.

Air travel is the safest form of transport. Travel by car is the most lethal. Buses and trains are also very safe. According to the United States National Safety Council. over the decade between 2010 and 2020 the death rate for people travelling by car per 100,000,000 passenger kilometres was over ten times higher than for buses, 17 times higher than for passenger trains, and 1623 times higher than for scheduled airlines.

CHAPTER 12

THE ARTS, MUSIC, AND FILMS

What happened to van Gogh's ear?

Artist Vincent van Gogh is famous for many things, including paintings *The Starry Night* and *Vase with Fifteen Sunflowers*. However, he was also the epitome of the tortured artist, eventually taking his own life in 1890. He achieved notoriety for, amid the depths of one bout of mania, cutting off all or some of his left ear (it's still a matter of dispute). The episode is well documented, but what happened to the ear? One story has it that he wrapped it in newspaper and took it to a nearby brothel in Arles, asked for a woman called Rachel, and gave it to her, telling her to "guard it safely". At that point she fainted. Another, more favoured, story says it was given to a cleaner, Gabrielle Berlatier, who worked in the same building and that she possibly sold it on to pay medical bills after she was bitten by a rabid dog. Its current where-abouts is unknown.

In 2014, a "living replica" of van Gogh's ear went on display at the Centre for Art and Media in Karlsruhe, Germany. It's made from the actual cells and DNA of the artist's brother's great-great-grandson and was grown by "biodesigner" Diemut Strebe, who then used a 3D printer to create the ear shape.

Before his death van Gogh sold only one painting: *The Red Vineyard*, for 400 francs (or about £15).

* * *

In the original *Star Trek* series, Captain Kirk never said, "Beam me up, Scotty." It's now a popular idiom used to mean an embarrassed speaker would really prefer to be somewhere else.

Nor, for that matter, did Kirk's science officer Mr Spock ever say, "It's life, Jim, but not as we know it." The words do, however, appear in *Star Trekkin'*, a song by British band The Firm.

The name of the "phasers" used in *Star Trek* is an acronym of "phased energy rectification".

Playwright William Shakespeare is even more misquoted than the crew of the Starship Enterprise. The most famous

Shakespeare misquote is probably "All that glitters is not gold." The message discovered by the Prince of Morocco in *The Merchant of Venice* actually says "All that glisters is not gold."

Shakespeare's witches in *Macbeth*, while mixing their cauldron, are often misquoted as saying "Hubble, bubble, toil, and trouble." But that might surprise the Bard because in his play they actually say "Double, double, toil, and trouble." You can decide for yourself whether that is an improvement.

Sherlock Holmes, Sir Arthur Conan Doyle's fictional detective, never said, "Elementary, my dear Watson" to his long-suffering but trusty sidekick Dr John Watson. Canadian Mark Alberstat, an expert on the world's most famous supersleuth, told me: "Holmes doesn't say, 'Elementary, my dear Watson' at any point in the original stories, although he does in TV shows and films. He uses the term 'elementary' several times when describing some of his deductions and he also says, 'My dear Watson' frequently. But never together."

In 1803 Italian physician Giovanni Aldini arrived in London searching for a corpse. He acquired the body of George Forster, a murderer hanged at Newgate Prison. In the lecture theatre at the Royal Institution on Albemarle Street he attached Forster's spine to an electric current. His plan was to bring Forster back to life. The body arched and appeared to sit bolt upright. Forster, of course, didn't really come back from the dead but it's possible that a young writer, Mary Shelley, whose father knew people who had witnessed Aldini's demonstration, became fascinated with the story and *Frankenstein*, her most famous book published in 1818, was the result.

Ironically, the book most stolen from public libraries is *The Guinness Book of Records*, which means that it will find itself mentioned within its own covers.

Perhaps even more ironically, the book that is most stolen from any source is the Bible. But to be fair, there are often stacks of them available for free (if not necessarily legally) at places of worship, so maybe the temptation is simply greater.

The best-selling single novel of all time is Charles Dickens's *A Tale of Two Cities*, first published in 1859. It has sold more than 200 million copies.

Even though it is split into 13 volumes, Marcel Proust's epic *À la recherché du temps perdu* (or *In Search of Lost Time*) has almost 1.3 million words, or 9,609,000 characters. Written between 1913 and 1927, in some editions, it has a page count of more than 3000.

The world's smallest book is *Teeny Ted from Turnip Town*, which can only be read through an electron microscope. The book was written by Malcolm Douglas Chaplin and produced in the Nano Imaging Laboratory at Simon

Fraser University in Vancouver, Canada. It is 0.07 milli-metres wide and 0.10 millimetres tall and its letters are carved into 30 microtablets on crystalline silicon. It even has its own ISBN. There are 100 copies in existence.

American writer Mark Twain was born in 1835, the year of an appearance of Halley's Comet. He died in the year of its next appearance, 1910, when Twain was 74. It's worth noting that tens of thousands of other people around the world died in 1910 aged 74, which makes the coincidence somewhat less striking.

In 1989, Ayatollah Ruhollah Khomeini issued a fatwa condemning Salman Rushdie to death for alleged blas-phemy in his novel *The Satanic Verses*. Salman Rushdie has survived two assassination attempts by Mustafa Mahmoud Mazeh (1989) and Hadi Matar (2022).

Rock guitarist Jimi Hendrix (at number 23) and classical composer Georg Friedrich Händel (at number 25) were next-door neighbours in Brook Street in Mayfair, London. Or they would have been, had they lived in the same century. They do share a museum, though, with the two addresses combined to form Handel Hendrix House.

The first recorded Punch and Judy show appeared in the diary of Samuel Pepys in London on 9 May, 1662.

People who find clowns sinister are known as coulro-phobics.

Based on internet searches, the top five most inexplicable and confusing films are:

2001: A Space Odyssey (nobody has a clue what the ending means).

Inception (it takes place inside a character's mind with other characters sharing an interconnected dream space. Enough said . . .).

Fight Club (it uses soap as a metaphor for cleansing humanity of its consumerism).

Mulholland Drive (involving a woman who has amnesia following a car crash, it takes place on three overlapping levels – the subconscious, dreams, and reality. And you never figure out which is which).

Tenet (a CIA agent has learnt how to manipulate time, known as inversion. There are scenes from the film's first half involving characters who have inverted time to "rewind" from the second half. Unsurprisingly, 70,000 people a month turn to the internet to figure out what it all means).

Both *Inception* and *Tenet* are directed by Christopher Nolan.

Plan Z from Outer Space is frequently designated "the worst film ever made". Its errors are legion and include day changing to night in the same scene many times; pictures on a wall changing during a phone call; a police car changing model mid-scene; furniture moving; pilots in a plane sitting on boxes not chairs; bodies in a grave-yard that are clearly shop mannequins; voices not in synch with mouth movements; an actor brushing a stage tree which rocks; crew equipment such as spotlights, cameras, and booms appearing in shot; scenes of a military attack using stock footage of the Korean War; flying saucers that are clearly plates or hub caps lobbed into the air or hung on strings; actors accidentally knocking over tomb-stones in a graveyard; and characters getting each other's names wrong. And that's just for starters.

The longest word to appear in any Shakespeare work is honorificabilitudinitatibus, which appears in *Love's Labour's Lost*. It has 27 letters and means the state of being able to achieve honours.

The *Mona Lisa* by Leonardo da Vinci is the world's most valuable painting. In 1962, its insurance value was US $100 million, which is equal to $1 billion today. The painting has hung in the Louvre in Paris since 1797 and been subject to multiple theft and vandalism attempts with acid, razor blades, red paint, rocks, and a mug of coffee. In 1911 it was stolen by Vincenzo Peruggia, an Italian patriot who thought the painting should be returned to Italy. Artist Pablo Picasso was also in the, er, frame for the crime until Peruggia was nabbed. While it was missing, people queued to see the empty space on the wall. Most recently in 2022, a man disguised as a woman in a wheelchair threw a cake at the painting to protest against climate change.

The Mona Lisa has her own mailbox at the Louvre because she receives so many love letters.

Salvador Dali got the idea for the melting clocks that are so often depicted in his paintings from watching wheels of Camembert cheese melting in the sun.

The first word Pablo Picasso spoke was "lápiz", or "pencil".

New York City I, a painting by Dutch artist Piet Mondrian was put on display at New York's MoMA gallery in 1945. In 2022 it was discovered that it had been hanging upside down for 77 years.

Although Guinness World Records no longer has a category for loudest rock band for fear of promoting hearing loss, a volume of 139 decibels was achieved by American heavy metal band Manowar during a sound check for a concert in 2008.

When British band Deep Purple set an earlier record of 117 decibels at London's Rainbow Theatre in 1972, three audience members were rendered unconscious.

Artist Willard Wigan makes microsculptures. They are so small they have to be viewed through a microscope. While he was making a sculpture of Alice from *Alice in Wonderland,* he accidentally breathed it in, swallowed it and had to make another. To do his work, Wigan slows his heart rate and works between the beats.

Statues in Roman times were designed with interchangeable heads in case anyone fell out of favour with the emperor.

Art historians can use the effects of the first nuclear bomb detonations to spot fakes. The explosions created new elements: strontium and caesium. So, if someone claims a painting is dated before 1945 and you can find traces of these two elements in it, it is likely to be a fake.

Photographer Patrick Hall decided he wanted to make slow-motion videos of people's faces when they were being tasered. Astonishingly, he found enough volunteers for his 2014 installation.

Chinese artist He Yunchang believes true art requires suffering. He's done all of the following:

Had a rib removed so that he could wear it as a necklace.

Encased himself in a cube of concrete for 24 hours.

Burnt his clothes while wearing them.

Painted the fingernails and toenails of ten mannequins with his own blood.

Stared at a powerful light bulb to damage his eyesight.

MYTH BUSTING

Myth: Spain's national anthem is the only one without words.

It is actually one of four. The anthems of Bosnia and Herzegovina, Kosovo, and San Marino also don't have words.

CHAPTER 13

SPORT

Why are there two types of rugby?

A surprising number of people don't realise it, but there are two sports called rugby. There's rugby league and there's rugby union. Back in the 19th century, rugby – invented at Rugby School in Warwickshire – was mainly the preserve of public schools and their well-to-do alumni. Following the Industrial Revolution, however, the game became popular in working-class communities in the north of England. In those days, matches were most often played on Saturdays, which was a working day in factories and mines. Rugby, at that time, was a strictly amateur sport so, when in the late 1880s the northern clubs asked the governing body in London – the Rugby Football Union (RFU) – if players could be compensated for "broken time" (missing work shifts to play for their clubs), the answer was a resounding no. The president of the RFU, Arthur Budd, said: "If the working man cannot afford the leisure to play a game, he must do without it." Professionalism was against the rules and players who were paid were banned for life. The dispute came to a head on 29 August, 1895, when a group of 22 northern clubs broke away to form what was first called the Northern Union, later becoming the Rugby Football League. It is known as "the great schism" and it saw both sports at loggerheads for a century, with peace only breaking out when rugby union turned professional almost 100 years to the day after rugby league, on 26 August, 1995.

The animosity between the two was so great that for 100 years anyone who played, or sometimes simply watched, rugby league, even as an amateur, was banned for life from playing rugby union.

Rugby league was banned in British universities until 1969 and in the British armed forces until 1994. Governments even banned rugby league – the most notable examples being the Nazi-backed Vichy government in France in the Second World War and the apartheid government in South Africa, who both considered rugby league "degenerate".

After the great rugby schism, at first both codes played to the same rules. But slowly rugby league diverged from rugby union as it tried to make the game more entertaining. It needed to attract paying spectators now its players were being remunerated. Which is why we now have two different sports.

* * *

Forward passes are illegal in both codes of rugby. Yet most passes travel forward. So how? The simplest explanation is that if a player is running forward at 20 kilometres per hour and passes the ball backwards at a speed of 15 kilometres per hour to a supporting player, the ball is still travelling forwards relative to the ground at 5 kilometres per hour (20–15 = 5). Seen from above, the player catching the ball would take it in front of from where it was passed, even though the pass would look entirely legitimate to anyone watching. The rules of both rugby codes allow for this anomaly because the game would be unplayable if not. It's also the reason why forward passes cannot be adjudicated on by the video referee, because when shown in slow motion the anomaly becomes far more apparent.

In November, 1990, in a rugby league match against Sheffield Eagles, St Helens prop forward John Harrison threw the ball into the air and headed it into the in-goal area, where it was touched down for a try by his teammate, George Mann. The Sheffield players complained to the referee but it turned out Harrison's header didn't break any rule. Days later, the laws were amended to outlaw heading.

Tour de France cyclists consume around 6000 calories a day and 8000 on mountain stages.

Lewis Hamilton is the only black driver out of almost 800 to have competed in Formula 1. He is also the most successful ever. His tally in August, 2023 is 104 pole positions, 103 victories, and seven World Championship titles.

When the United States beat England 1–0 at football's 1950 men's World Cup in Belo Horizonte, Brazil, the English press arrogantly presumed that an error had been made when the result was transmitted by telegraph. Many newspapers reported it as 10–1 to England. The US scorer was Joe Gaetjens, who had been born in Haiti. It was the only international goal he ever scored.

England – the birthplace of football – has still never beaten the USA in a World Cup game (suffering one loss and two draws).

Although Americans and Australians call it soccer and the British don't, soccer was a word invented in England, not the US. It's short for association football and was used in England's aristocratic public schools, where sports were first codified to distinguish the game from rugby football (or rugger).

Otávio Jordão da Silva Cantanhede was a Brazilian football referee. When, on 30 June, 2013, he attempted to send off a player, Josemir Santos Abreu, the latter refused to leave the field. So da Silva stabbed him to death. At which point fans, including Abreu's family, invaded the pitch, decapitated da Silva and stuck his head on a stake.

In 2001, Brian Savill was refereeing a football match in Essex, in England, between Earls Colne and Wimpole. The score was 18–1 to Earls Colne and he was bored. The ball came close to him and he deliberately shot and scored. For Wimpole. "I felt sorry for them," he said. "We felt a bit patronised," said the Wimpole coach. Mr Savill was banned for seven weeks.

The Corinthians football team of the 19th century believed themselves to be gentlemen committed to upholding principles of fair play. They deemed that all foul play must surely have been accidental so, if they were ever awarded a penalty, they refused to score from it.

No player has been sent off more than Colombian footballer Gerardo Bedoya. In a 20-year career ending in 2015, he received 46 red cards in 601 matches. He moved into management and was sent off on his coaching debut in 2016.

Bananas were so rare in East Germany, and usually only found in Berlin, that supporters of football teams from the city used to take them to away matches and wave them to taunt opposition supporters.

The fastest ball in sport is found in the Basque game of pelota. Speeds of more than 300 kilometres an hour have been measured. That's as fast as a Formula 1 car.

Of approximately 2500 international test cricket matches that have been played since 1877, only two have ended in ties – Australia v West Indies in 1960 and India v Australia in 1986.

When cricket umpires' decisions are challenged and referred to a third umpire, who has video footage, 26% of the original on-field decisions are overturned.

There are ten ways a batter can be out at cricket. In the entire history of international test cricket, only one person has been given out for "obstructing the field" (England's Len Hutton in 1951) and only one person has been given out for "hitting the ball twice" (Kurt Wilkinson of Barbados in 2002). No player has ever been "timed out" (that is, not entering the field of play quickly enough after the previous batter was out).

Baseball umpires are required to wear black underwear in case their trousers split.

Aroldis Chapman of the Cincinnati Reds holds the record for the fastest baseball pitch of 170.3 kilometres per hour in 2010.

42,000 tennis balls are used at Wimbledon every year.

The fastest cricket ball bowled was by Pakistan's Shoaib Akhtar, at 161.3 kilometres per hour in 2003.

A spinning cricket ball can rotate more than 50 times after it leaves the bowlers' hand and before it reaches the batter (a distance of around 20 metres). That's getting on for 3000 revolutions per minute.

Table-tennis balls can travel off the bat at around 170 kilometres per hour.

A Formula 1 car creates so much downforce that it can drive upside down on a tunnel roof.

The fastest shot recorded in a football match was Brazilian Ronny Heberson's 210 kilometre-per-hour free kick while playing for Sporting Lisbon in 2006. The fastest shot in open play came from Arjen Robben, who clocked 190 kilometres an hour in 2009 while playing for Real Madrid.

In 1994 Bulgaria's national football team played a match where all the players' surnames ended in "ov".

Great sporting nicknames:

  The Wild Bull of the Pampas (Vince Karalius, rugby league)

  The Lion of Vienna (Nat Lofthouse, football)

The Owl Without a Vowel (Bill Mlkvy, basketball)

The Flying Housewife (Fanny Blankers-Koen, athletics)

The Round Mound of Rebound (Charles Barkley, basketball)

The Monza Gorilla (Vittorio Brambilla – because it rhymes, motor racing)

Slabhead (Harry Maguire, football)

Two sports can pinpoint the exact date on which they were invented. Basketball, created by Canadian James Naismith on 21 December, 1891, and rugby league, at the George Hotel, Huddersfield on 29 August, 1895.

There is a perfect voice for sports commentary based on pitch, overall loudness, variability of loudness, rhythm, tone, and constriction. When these are all scored out of 10, the presenter with the best total was the late John Motson, the BBC's former football commentator.

Netball, a game primarily played by women, was invented in England as a response to basketball. Because in polite Victorian society women wore ankle-length skirts and starchy blouses, dribbling a ball and running was difficult. The rules were adapted so a similar game could be played without.

Heavyweight boxing champion George Foreman named all his five sons George. He also named a daughter Georgetta.

The greatest comeback in Wimbledon tennis history was by American player and former champion Jimmy Connors in 1987. 1–6, 1–6, and 1–4 down to Sweden's Mikael Pernfors in the third set, he came back to win 1–6, 1–6, 7–5, 6–4, 6–2.

The longest-ever tennis match was between American John Isner and French player Nicolas Mahut at Wimbledon in 2010. It lasted over three days and took 11 hours and 5 minutes, with Isner triumphing in the last set by 70 games to 68.

So who's the biggest cheat in sport? Well, Lance Armstrong doped his way to seven Tour de France victories between 1999 and 2005, all now expunged from the records, so he likely has a bigger claim than most. But here's a few others who run him close:

Ben Johnson: The Canadian won the 100 metres at the 1988 Olympics in Seoul and set a new world record. But if his yellowing eyes hinting at an overload of his liver didn't give the game away, his post-race urine samples did.

Diego Maradona: The Argentinian footballer may have scored what is considered the greatest goal ever in a World Cup later in the same match, but that's no consolation to a few million English fans who couldn't believe the referee missed Maradona scoring his first goal by punching it into the net. He called it "the hand of God". Argentina beat England 2–1 and went on to win the 1986 World Cup. Maradona also once falsified a drugs test by using a fake penis filled with another person's urine.

Boris Onishchenko: The Soviet athlete was having a great day in the Modern Pentathlon's fencing discipline at the 1976 Montreal Olympics, winning bout after bout. That's until he came up against Great Britain's Jim Fox. Fox realised he was losing points without being hit. He ripped off Onishchenko's sword to reveal a hidden button that the fencer was pressing to record spurious scores.

Cheating is deliberate, mishaps are accidental. But both occur regularly in sport. In 1967, Leeds United were playing Liverpool in English football's First Division. Leeds goalkeeper Gary Sprake collected the ball and went to throw it to one of his outfield players. Except he changed his mind mid-throw and, losing control, lobbed it into the back of his own goal.

Sprake has rivals for his crown, however:

Jean van der Velde: At the 1999 Open Golf Championship at Carnoustie in Scotland, the Frenchman held what seemed an unassailable three-shot lead as he teed off at the 18th and last hole. His first shot somehow landed on the 17th, rather than the 18th fairway. His second hit a grandstand and ended in the rough. His third landed in a stream. His fourth was a dropped ball. His fifth landed in a bunker. His sixth finally landed on the green. And his seventh went into the hole. Unsurprisingly, he didn't win.

Don Fox: In the last minute of rugby league's 1968 Challenge Cup Final, the Wakefield Trinity player had the simplest of kicks right in front of the posts to win the match. It was wet, he scuffed it wide, fell to the turf in tears, and commentator Eddie Waring called him a "poor lad". It guaranteed Fox fame (or infamy). You can still buy a T-shirt with "poor lad" written across the front.

Gordon Smith: It was 2–2 between Brighton and Hove Albion and Manchester United in the 1983 FA Cup Final when, in the last minute, Brighton's Gordon Smith was through on goal with the simplest of chances. "And Smith must score," screamed commentator Peter Jones. He didn't and, like Fox before him, became immortalised, this time in the name of Brighton's fanzine *And Smith Must Score*.

The state sport of Maryland is jousting.

Usain Bolt's maximum recorded speed is an astonishing 44.72 kph. It's the fastest speed clocked by a human and it was recorded between the 60- and 80-metre marks of the 2009 World Athletics Championships 100 metres final.

Fishing is the biggest participation sport on the planet.

Five-times Formula 1 world champion Juan Manuel Fangio of Argentina was kidnapped by revolutionary leader Fidel Castro in Cuba while in Havana for the 1958 Cuban Grand Prix. Fangio got on well with Castro's revolutionaries and was released unharmed. He received a Christmas card from them every year until his death in 1995.

The most popular sport among nudists is volleyball.

Lawman and gambler James Butler, better known as Wild Bill Hickok, was shot dead by Jack Macall in 1876 while playing poker in a saloon in South Dakota. He was holding two black aces, two black eights (and the jack of diamonds). Since then two black eights and two black aces plus a holding card has been known as "the dead man's hand".

MYTH BUSTING

Myth: William Webb Ellis invented rugby.

The story goes that in 1823, "with a fine disregard for the rules of football as played in his time", a pupil at Rugby School picked up the ball "and ran with it". That pupil was Webb Ellis but the story is almost certainly a myth. Webb Ellis was a Rugby School pupil but no one mentioned his rule-breaking until 1876 when another pupil, Matthew Bloxam, wrote about it in the school magazine. Bloxam admitted he did not witness the event. The story came to light again in 1895, the year the two rugby codes (league and union) split and ownership of the game was in the balance. An inquiry was held by the school that year to discover who invented rugby but it couldn't find any evidence it was Webb Ellis. Yet it still declared that he did, and subsequently a plaque was erected at the school, identifying it as the sport's birthplace. It was possibly an attempt by rugby union to assert ownership of the game from the upstart rugby league. "That may be so," says Phil McGowan, curator of the World Rugby Museum at Twickenham, "although we currently have no proof either way. However, the first written laws of any football code were those produced at Rugby School in 1845."

Myth: The first international cricket match was between Australia and England.

The test match between Australia and England in Melbourne in 1877 is often cited as being the first-ever international cricket match. It wasn't. In 1844 – that's 33 years earlier – the USA played Canada at St George's Cricket Club in New York. Canada won by 23 runs.

CHAPTER 14

SPACE EXPLORATION

400,171 kilometres from Earth.

During their aborted moon landing mission in 1970 the astronauts of Apollo 13 – Jim Lovell, Jack Swigert and Fred Haise – were forced to orbit the Moon, using its gravity to point them back in the direction of Earth. On 14 April, they were 400,171 kilometres from Earth. Nobody else has travelled so far from home.

* * *

Buzz Aldrin was the first man to do two things on the Moon. He peed and he prayed. Strangely, the latter proved more controversial. When the Apollo 11 astronaut – the second man to walk on the Moon after Neil Armstrong, and a devout Presbyterian – took communion, he was following in the footsteps of the Apollo 8 astronauts, who had recited from the Bible after being the first people to orbit the Moon. That infuriated Madalyn Murray O'Hair, founder of American Atheists, who filed a lawsuit against the US government, alleging that the reading of religious texts by astronauts – who are government employees – was a violation of the US Constitution, which guarantees the separation of church and state. Murray lost the case but Aldrin later admitted that he'd inadvertently caused controversy and wished he hadn't.

On 14 December, 1972, Eugene Cernan (the only member of that high-speed Apollo 10 crew (see page 100) eventually to land on the Moon) became the last of 12 men to tread the lunar surface. He departed the Moon saying that humans would be returning "not too long into the future" and that we would have landed on Mars by 2000. He was very wrong – the next humans to visit the Moon are slated to return in 2025. And no human has set foot on Mars yet.

Spaceships slingshotting around a planet, using its gravity to increase speed, is a regular trope of science fiction. But it's also science fact too. On 5 March, 1979, Voyager 1 used the gravitational fields of Jupiter and Saturn to speed it on its way to the edge of the solar system. But in physics you don't get something for nothing. Because Voyager's speed was increased, this meant that the rotation of Jupiter slowed and it moved closer to the Sun by about the diameter of a proton, or approximately one-millionth of a nanometre.

SPACE EXPLORATION

Only four men who walked on the Moon are still alive: Buzz Aldrin, David Scott, Charlie Duke, and Harrison Schmitt. Everybody who has walked on the Moon has been American, white, and male.

Because there is no atmosphere to erode them, Neil Armstrong's footprints on the Moon will last for millions of years.

Astronauts grow taller in space. The lack of gravity allows their spines to expand and they grow on average by 5 centimetres. If you visit the International Space Station, you'd better watch your head.

Sergei Krikalev went into space as a citizen of the Soviet Union on 19 May, 1991. He returned as a citizen of Russia on 25 March, 1992. Between his ascent and descent the Soviet Union was dissolved on 26 December, 1991, making him the first person to change nationality while in space.

When Krikalev returned, he was 0.02 of a second younger than he would have been had he stayed on Earth. That's because of time dilation. The motion of an object slows time – the faster you go, the slower time gets. It was predicted by Albert Einstein in his special theory of relativity and has been proven by clocks carried on airliners. They tick ever so slightly slower than identical ones on the ground.

Valeri Polyakov holds the record for the longest single stay in space – 473 days 18 hours aboard the Mir space station between 8 January, 1994 and 22 March, 1995.

Astronauts lose between 1% and 2% of their bone mineral density for every month spent in space, because they are no longer using their bones to support their bodies. It's known as spaceflight osteopenia and because nobody has spent long enough in space yet, we don't know if it continues indefinitely. Doctors are using the information gleaned from astronauts who recover from osteopenia to treat patients with osteoporosis – or brittle and fragile bones – here on Earth.

Space is dangerous. It probably goes without saying. But, quite astonishingly, nobody has ever died there. All the humans – with the possible exception of the crew of Soyuz 11 – who have perished during missions were either going to or returning from space, still within the Earth's atmosphere. The first was Soviet cosmonaut Vladimir Komarov, the first person to fly in space twice. In 1967, his Soyuz 1 capsule failed to deploy its solar panels, meaning its power was depleted. Many times Komarov attempted to orient the capsule so it would re-enter the atmosphere at the correct angle. By the time he did so, the spacecraft's parachute was damaged. It smashed into the ground, travelling at 40 metres per second. Komarov's case was especially tragic. Imagine being inside a capsule no bigger than a telephone box, knowing for hours that your end was nigh. By the time he died, mission control suspected Komarov had gone insane. The most recent space fatalities were the crew of the US space shuttle Columbia as it returned from a mission on 1 February. 2003. A damaged heat shield caused the spacecraft to break up as it re-entered the atmosphere. This disaster and that of the space shuttle Challenger in 1986 account for 14 of the 19 deaths attributed to spaceflight. More than 650 people have flown in space, meaning the fatality rate is approaching 3%.

It is possible the three-man crew of Soyuz 11 was the first to die in space in 1971. A cabin vent accidentally opened on the spacecraft's return from the Salyut 1 space station, draining the cabin of air either just outside, or just inside Earth's atmosphere.

Salyut 1 was the first space station ever built. It was launched in April 1971 and first occupied on 7 June.

The only other time, aside from the space shuttle and Soyuz 1 tragedies, that more than one person died in a space-related accident was during testing for the flight of Apollo 1 in 1967. An electrical fire in the capsule's cabin, which spread quickly in the pure oxygen atmosphere, killed US astronauts Ed White, Gus Grissom, and Roger Chaffee.

The Voyager 1 space probe became the first human-built object to cross the heliosphere (in August 2012), which marks the edge of our solar system and the start of outer space.

In August 2018, a hole was found in the International Space Station. It had been drilled from the inside, by whom and for what reason was never discovered (or at least the outcome of any investigation was never published).

On 26 November, 2022, the uncrewed Artemis 1 spacecraft, which will carry humans to the Moon in 2025, reached 432,194 kilometres from Earth. Artemis is also more powerful than the rocket that took Apollo to the Moon. Maybe the records of Apollo 10 and Apollo 13 will soon be broken.

In 2024, Japan intends to launch a satellite made of wood. The last item of space hardware to use wood in its construction was the 1962 Ranger 5 space probe, which intended to use a balsawood casing to cushion the blow of landing on the Moon. Unfortunately, it missed the Moon, meaning that a block of wood with expensive hardware inside is now somewhere orbiting the Sun.

The first meal eaten in space was beef and liver paste in 1961. The first human in space, the Soviet Union's Yuri Gagarin, squeezed it from a tube while orbiting the Earth. The first American astronaut to eat in space was John Glenn in 1962. He ate apple sauce, also from a tube.

Space travel dulls taste and smell and all space food is processed, not fresh. This means the most common luxuries demanded by astronauts are mustard and Tabasco sauce.

The Moon-walking Apollo astronauts claim that it smells of wet ashes or gunpowder. John Young of Apollo 16 is said to have eaten a piece and that, although it didn't taste of cheese, it wasn't too bad. Other astronauts have reported that space itself smells slightly of burned steak.

In 2013 cosmonaut Pavel Vinogrodov thought that by being in space he would be able to avoid paying his taxes. He couldn't. The Russian tax authorities pointed out that the International Space Station had internet access and demanded he pay up.

MYTH BUSTING

Myth: Your blood boils if you are beamed into space (without a spacesuit).

Despite space not being a total vacuum (see page 17), it's totally deadly to humans. There's no air to breathe, the (almost) vacuum means the air will be pushed out of your lungs and other cavities because your body is at such high pressure compared to your low-pressure surroundings. And eventually you'll freeze solid. But your blood won't boil. The boiling point of liquids is reduced if the air pressure is reduced. Therefore even though space is very cold, liquids boil in the low pressure. But not your blood. This is almost certainly a myth invented by Hollywood for graphic effect. Your blood is contained within your closed circulatory system and so is protected from what's going on outside. You'll still die, though.

Myth: The United States won the space race.

It depends how you define winning. When the United States and the Soviet Union began putting humans into orbit, it was part of a propaganda war. Which ideology was better – communism or capitalism? It culminated on 20 July, 1969, when the US put a human on the Moon, as Neil Armstrong took his "one small step for a man". Apollo 11's successful mission has since come to define victory as belonging to the US but, for most of the previous decade and more, the Americans were chasing the Soviets. In October, 1957, the Soviet Union launched the world's first artificial satellite, Sputnik 1; in 1961, Yuri Gagarin became the first man to fly in space; in 1963, Valentina Tereshkova became the first woman to do the same, and is still the only woman to have flown a solo mission (the first American female in space was Sally Ride, 20 years later); and in 1965, Alexei Leonov became the first person to conduct extravehicular activity, or a spacewalk. Perhaps if victory, like boxing matches, is judged on points, there's a case to be made for the USSR. Or Germany ... *Germany?*

Myth: The Soviet satellite Sputnik 1 was the first human-made object to fly in space in 1957.

The Soviet Union may have launched the first artificial satellite into orbit in 1957 but Sputnik 1 wasn't the first human-built object to fly in space. The world's first intercontinental ballistic missile was developed in Nazi Germany and launched against Paris, London, and other cities in September 1944. At their highest altitude, V2s crossed the Kármán Line – the boundary between Earth's atmosphere and space. This was achieved during testing on 20 June, 1944, a full 13 years before Sputnik was launched.

A V2 also took the first photograph from space when a captured rocket with a camera attached to its nose was launched from White Sands Missile Range in New Mexico on 24 October, 1946. For the first time the curvature of the Earth was recorded on film.

Myth: Yuri Gagarin was the first man in space.

Well, actually he was, but not according to the rules. It was widely accepted that the first spaceflight should comprise a human launching from the ground in their spacecraft, orbiting the Earth outside the atmosphere, and returning to Earth still within their capsule. On 12 April, 1961, Gagarin went up OK, orbited the earth OK (in 108 minutes), and set Vostok 1 for re-entry. But his re-entry vehicle failed to separate from its equipment module and the two parts of the spacecraft began gyrating wildly. At seven kilometres altitude Gagarin decided to bale out with his parachute and landed ten minutes later. Fortunately, even though he didn't really play by the rules, most of us are happy to accept Gagarin *was* the first man in space.

Gagarin only found out he would be the first four days before he flew. His closest rival for the flight was Gherman Titov – both were diminutive, the Vostok 1 capsule was very cramped – but the latter was deemed too bourgeois and Gagarin's impeccable working-class credentials got him the nod. Titov did set one record, though, he was the first person to be sick in space.

Myth: Laika the dog was the first animal in space.

Actually, she wasn't. We realise this is beginning to sound repetitive but another famous space first isn't actually correct. Using a captured V2, American scientists launched a group of fruit flies (*Drosophila melanogaster*) into space on 20 February, 1947. They survived the journey too. After that they sent up a few mice and a few monkeys, none of which did. Laika was, however, the first animal to fully orbit the Earth in Sputnik 2 on 3 November, 1957. Unfortunately, she also didn't survive. Animal ethics were notably different in that era.

Myth: Tang was invented for the US space programme.

Nope. Tang is an orange-flavoured powder that's added to water to make a drink. When John Glenn became the first American to orbit the Earth in 1962, he pointed out that his Mercury capsule's onboard water system tasted foul. NASA's answer was Tang, but they didn't invent it; it was already on America's supermarket shelves. Unsurprisingly, the makers of Tang played up the association to the point where it became widely believed it had been invented for space travel. There's one school of thought that says Tang tastes worse than the original water supply, but that is, of course, subjective.

Myth: Velcro was invented for the US space programme.

Again, nope. It had been around since the 1940s, when it was created by a Swiss engineer George de Mestral ("Velcro" is short for *velours crochet*, French for "velvet hook"). Astronauts did find it exceptionally useful for sticking things to walls in zero gravity, however.

Myth: Space pens were invented for the US space programme.

Thrice nope. The story goes that US scientists spent years and millions of dollars trying to design a pen that would write upside down and in zero gravity. And then they discovered that the Soviet Union had simply given their cosmonauts a pencil. If only it were true. By 1965, the Fisher Pen Company had already invented pens that would write upside down, in extreme temperatures, and under water. Fisher simply offered their pens to NASA at $2.39 each. The Soviet Union bought some too because they realised wooden pencils were inflammable and graphite specks from the writing tip could get into sensitive equipment.

CHAPTER 15

THE WEATHER

Why does tarmac smell when it rains?

That warm, earthy aroma following rainfall after a long dry spell is caused by bacteria. A chemical called geosmin is produced by Streptomyces, which can be found in dry soils all over the world. When the raindrops strike the ground, geosmin is released into the air. The scent actually has a name – petrichor – and geosmin is used in some perfumes.

* * *

At any one time there are approximately 2000 thunderstorms raging on Earth.

Flies don't get swamped by rain because they are so light that the pressure wave ahead of a falling raindrop – similar to the wind you can feel from an approaching underground train – pushes the fly out of the way.

Officially, the largest hailstone on record measured 20.3 centimetres in diameter and 27.3 centimetres in circumference, and weighed 0.88 kilograms. It fell on the town of Vivian, South Dakota on 23 July, 2010. An enormous hailstone measuring as much as 23.6 centimetres in diameter fell on Villa Carlos Paz in Argentina in 2018 but was only shown on social media and not officially verified.

Hailstones can fall at speeds of up to 175 kilometres per hour, easily enough to concuss or kill a human.

Raindrops tend to be restricted in size by collision and instabilities across their surfaces to about 6 millimetres in diameter, although in warmer conditions they can reach 8 millimetres.

Meteorologists use the diameter and the reflectivity of raindrops using radar to estimate the volume of rain in a shower.

Arica in Chile is the driest place on earth. For over 14 years, from October, 1903 to January, 1918, Arica saw no rainfall – a drought of 173 months. On average it receives 0.76 millimetres of precipitation a year.

By contrast, Mawsynram in Meghalaya state, India holds the world record for the most precipitation received annually on average: 11,872 millimetres. Yes, that's nearly 12 metres a year.

On 26 November, 1970, 38 millimetres of rain fell in Sainte-Anne, Guadeloupe in just one minute.

The most rain recorded in 24 hours was the 1825 millimetres that fell on Cilaos, on the island of Réunion, between 7 and 8 January, 1966.

Valentine's Day was presumably ruined (or perhaps enhanced?) on 14 February, 1927, when 230 centimetres of snow fell on Mount Ibuki, Japan, the most recorded in a single day.

The largest snowball ever rolled was by students from ASME Michigan Technological University in the US on 29 March, 2013. It measured 10.04 metres in circumference and presumably wouldn't have been much use in a snowball fight.

The largest storm ever recorded on Earth was Typhoon Tip in 1979. It spanned 2220 kilometres – that's almost the distance between London and Athens – and at its peak it spun at 305 kilometres per hour. When it hit Japan, it killed 86 people and destroyed 20,000 homes.

The fastest wind speed ever recorded (not including the incredible velocities found in tornadoes) was 408 kilometres per hour on Barrow Island, Australia as Tropical Cyclone Olivia passed over on 10 April, 1996.

While it is more difficult to measure wind speeds in the narrow confines of a tornado, it is believed that the 1999 Bridge Creek-Moore Tornado in Oklahoma on 3 May, 1999 reached speeds of between 490 and 510 kilometres per hour. This is the highest wind speed recorded on the surface of the Earth.

The biggest tornado outbreak occurred between 25 and 28 April, 2011, when 360 tornadoes were recorded across the southern states of the US (although some were confirmed as far north as New York state). The most active day was 27 April, which saw a record for a 24-hour period of 216 tornadoes.

The deadliest tornado ever recorded was the Daulatpur-Saturia Tornado of 1989, which killed approximately 1300 people in Bangladesh.

The windiest place on Earth is Port Martin in Antarctica, which averages more than 100 days every year with winds that exceed 65 kilometres per hour.

Due to the Coriolis effect (see page 76), hurricanes in the northern hemisphere spin in an anticlockwise direction, while hurricanes in the southern hemisphere spin in a clockwise direction.

They are not all called hurricanes, though; it depends where you live. The name "hurricane" is one of three used to describe giant, spiralling tropical storms with winds of at least 119 kilometres an hour. Hurricanes form over the north Atlantic, central north Pacific, and eastern north Pacific, but if they form over the south Pacific or the Indian Ocean, they are known as cyclones. And if they develop in the north-west Pacific they are called typhoons.

Based on Twitter usage, Britons complain more about the weather than the citizens of any other nation.

Why is the sky blue? The short answer is that when the Sun's light hits the Earth's atmosphere, it scatters – like light hitting a prism. And during daytime we generally inhabit the blue bit (although readers in the UK will doubt-less say "don't you mean the grey bit?"). Earlier in the day and in the evening, when the sunlight is effectively passing through more atmosphere, the sky will instead appear red or orange. The longer answer is that the process is called Rayleigh scattering. Light with higher frequencies (like blue) is scattered far more than light with lower frequencies (like red) when it hits the air mole-cules of our atmosphere.

The Sun is hotter at the Earth's equator than at the poles because the incoming solar radiation is more direct (it is nearly perpendicular). The curve of the Earth means that the sunlight is spread over a wider area the further you move from the equator and it strikes the Earth at a much narrower angle. The curvature also means there is more atmosphere for the sunlight to pass through at the poles compared to the equator. This means less heat from the Sun makes it to the surface of the Earth at the poles because it is absorbed and scattered by the atmosphere.

A single bolt of lightning on 29 April, 2020 stretched over 767 kilometres across Texas, Louisiana, and Mississippi in the USA. It was the longest bolt ever recorded.

The bolt with the longest duration also occurred the same year. On 18 June, 2020 a lightning flash ripped through the skies of Uruguay and northern Argentina, which lasted 17 seconds.

A single bolt of lightning contains enough energy to toast 100,000 pieces of sliced bread.

Between 1942 and 1977 Roy Sullivan, a ranger in the Shenandoah National Park in Virginia in the US, was struck by lightning seven times. He survived them all.

The odds of being struck by lightning seven times over the course of a lifetime are 1 in 10,000,000,000,000,000, 000,000,000,000. You can understand why poor old Roy Sullivan was peeved.

At any given time, around 67% of the Earth's surface is covered by clouds.

Cumulonimbus clouds produce hail, thunder, and lightning. The average weight of a cumulonimbus cloud is about 400,000 kilograms, similar to the weight of the Airbus A380 airliner, which usually does its best to avoid flying through them.

In 2017 it rained fish in Tampico in Mexico. And it's a relatively common event. Storms in coastal areas can create tornado-like waterspouts that suck water into the air, including whatever is in the water. The storms blow inland and fish come tumbling down. It's so commonplace in Yoro, a Honduran village, that they celebrate *lluvia de peces*, or rain of fish, annually.

Other animals that have fallen from the sky following waterspouts include frogs. In 2005 thousands of baby frogs landed in Odzaci in Serbia. Most survived and hopped away.

In 2008 and 2018 iguanas fell on Florida, but this time from trees. Below a certain temperature, cold-blooded iguanas' bodies shut down to protect them. They are still alive but unable to hold their grip and fall out of the trees they live in. When the weather warms up, they reactivate and amble away.

Florida also experienced golf-ball rain in 1969. A few hundred fell on the town of Punta Gorda. The only explanation is that bad golfers must have been hitting them into a lake on a nearby course where they had slowly been collecting until a waterspout struck the lake.

Perhaps even weirder rain occurred that same year. A powdered milk factory in South Carolina accidentally released its product into the air. It mixed with falling rain, which dumped sticky gloop all over the town of Chester.

MYTH BUSTING

Myth: There is controversy over whether humans are responsible for climate change.

No, there isn't. An overwhelming 97% of climate scientists agree that humans are the cause of global warming and climate change. More than 99.9% of peer-reviewed scientific papers agree that climate change is mainly caused by humans, according to a Cornell University survey of 88,125 climate-related studies. If the politicians who dispute global warming had approval ratings of 97%, they would not be calling into question the opinion-poll results.

According to greenmatters.com, the first climate-change protests took place on 22 April, 1970, known as the first Earth Day, when 20 million people across the US protested about the damage being done to our planet's environment.

Myth: We catch colds by going out in inclement weather.

Colds do become more prevalent in winter but they are not caused by cold weather. The only way to catch a cold is to catch a virus and these spread more easily in winter when people gather closely together inside, where it's warmer and more humid, exactly the kind of conditions that cold viruses like. You want further proof? People who work in polar regions never catch colds because the low temperatures kill viruses.

Snot is green because bacteria that infect your mucus are green in colour. When they proliferate and clump together, you start to see them. Some of the bacteria species are a golden colour – you may have noticed – while others, much rarer, are blue. All of which is rather disconcerting when you blow your nose.

Humans produce between 1 and 2 litres of nasal mucus a day but if you catch a cold, you can expect that to double. You swallow most of it.

CHAPTER 16

ROYALTY AND RELIGION

The Moon has a bishop.

The Vatican's 1917 Code of Canon Law states that, if a new territory is discovered, it becomes a diocese of the territory from which its discoverers left. Apollo 11, the first human mission to land on the Moon, launched from Cape Canaveral, which is in the diocese of Orlando. William Borders, the Catholic bishop of Orlando in 1969, therefore declared himself bishop of the Moon. There is no record of whether the Pope approved.

* * *

Early Christians used a fish, rather than a cross, to identify themselves. It is derived from Jesus Christ telling his apostle Peter that he would become a "fisher of men" if he followed his teachings.

The Mayans believed that turkeys were the vessels of gods and worshipped them accordingly.

Some early puritan branches of Christianity regarded forks as sacrilegious. They were regarded as "artificial hands" and, because real hands came from God, were considered an abomination.

On 16 February in 600 AD, Pope Gregory issued a papal decree requiring all Christians to utter the words "Bless you" when anybody sneezed. Sneezing was one of the first symptoms of the bubonic plague, which was sweeping Europe and would kill possibly as many as 50 million people.

Windsor Castle, in Berkshire, England is the oldest inhabited palace in the world (and the largest).

The reigning British monarch owns all Britain's unmarked swans, as well as whales, dolphins, and sturgeons, in British coastal waters. The law dates back to the 1300s.

The youngest-ever monarchs were both aged 0 when they ascended to their thrones. Jean I of France was born after the death of his father Louis X and so became king at the moment of his birth in 1316. Likewise, Alfonso XIII of Spain succeeded his father, Alfonso XII, posthumously in 1886.

The youngest English monarch was Henry VI, who was nine months old when he came to the throne in 1422, following the death of his father Henry V. He was also the only English king to be crowned king of France (although that's disputed by the French).

Henry VIII had servants known as Grooms of Stool. Their job was to wipe his bottom after he defecated. They deserved the knighthoods he granted them.

Number of kings executed by the English:
1 (Charles I).

Number of kings executed by the French:
1 (Louis XVI).

When Louis XVI and his wife Marie Antoinette were beheaded, people dipped handkerchiefs in their blood to keep as souvenirs. In 2011, scientists confirmed a stained handkerchief dated approximately 1793 – the year of his death – was soaked in the blood of Louis XVI.

At the time of his death in 1830, George IV weighed 152 kilograms (or 24 stones). His favourite breakfast – that's breakfast – consisted of two pigeons, three steaks, three quarters of a bottle of white wine, a glass of dry champagne, two glasses of port, and a glass of brandy.

The late Queen Elizabeth II's husband Prince Philip, the Duke of Edinburgh, was regarded as a god in two villages on the Vanuatuan island of Tanna. The people there believed him to be a recycled descendant of a powerful spirit that lived on a nearby mountaintop. The belief arose after an official visit to Vanuatu by the Queen and Prince Philip in 1974. The villagers noting the respect accorded to Philip decided that he was the fulfilment of a religious prophecy that had predicted one of their tribesmen would leave the island in his spiritual form to find a powerful wife overseas. On his death there was a period of official mourning with funeral rites. There is speculation over whether the villagers' veneration will now be transferred to Charles III.

Charles III, aged 74, is the oldest English monarch to be crowned. He is also the 42nd monarch since William I became king following the Norman Conquest of England in 1066. Only five have been women: Mary, Elizabeth I, Anne, Victoria, and Elizabeth II. However, Mary II ruled jointly with her husband William III.

British royals – or at least their travelling doctors – are expected to carry a bag of their own blood with them on trips abroad in case of emergency. The blood is red, not blue.

There are 43 countries in the world with a monarch as head of state. However, some share the same monarch. King Charles III is head of state of 15 of them.

Andorra is a unique form of monarchy. It is a co-princeship with the job shared between the President of France and the Bishop of Urgell in Spain. This means neither ruler actually lives in Andorra.

Brunei, Eswatini (formerly Swaziland), Oman, Saudi Arabia, Vatican City State, and the nations of the United Arab Emirates are the only remaining absolute monarchies. Absolute monarchies are those where the ruler's powers are unconstrained and unlimited by laws or a constitution.

In 2006 Harvard Medical School was involved in a study to see if prayers were actually effective. It concluded that they provided no benefit to the recovery of patients who had undergone cardiac bypass surgery. But, in an unexpected twist, patients who knew prayers were being said for them had more complications after surgery than those who didn't know. Doctors surmised that the complications could have been caused by the increased stress on patients worried that their conditions were so bad they needed prayers.

We have to give a shout out to Rastafari, designated the world's smallest organised religion with 0.6 million adherents. Compare that to the biggest, Christianity, with 2.382 billion, or 31.11% of the Earth's population. About half of all Christians are Roman Catholics.

Roman Catholics recognise more than 10,000 saints.

The Vatican and the Pitcairn Islands claim to be the only nations in the world where every citizen is a Christian. Similarly, Mauritania and the Maldives claim that their populations are 100% Muslim.

An estimated 83.4% of women around the world identify with a religion or other faith grouping, compared with 79.9% of men.

The Czech Republic has the highest number of atheists or agnostics at 78.4% of the population. By comparison, 31.2% of Britons fall into that category.

An estimated 1.2 billion people do not follow any religion. That's about 15% of the world's population.

Canada has a greater proportion of Sikhs per head of population than India does.

Mecca has a metro rail system built solely for the use of religious pilgrims. The Al Mashaaer Al Mugaddassah Metro, opened in November, 2010 in Saudi Arabia's holy city.

David Sheppard, the Church of England Bishop of Liverpool, played cricket for England between 1950 and 1963.

Father John Cootes was the first Roman Catholic priest to play international rugby league when he was selected for Australia to play New Zealand in 1969.

MYTH BUSTING

Myth: Easter eggs are Christian and are symbolic of the rebirth of Christ.

They may well be seen as such today but eggs were a common offering to the dead in Mesopotamia and Egypt, predating Christianity by as many as 3000 years. Painted ostrich eggs, gold and silver eggs, representing death and rebirth, have been found with entombed bodies.

CHAPTER 17

POLITICS

Albert Einstein could have been a head of state.

The famous scientist, best noted for his theories of general and special relativity, turned down the presidency of Israel in 1952 after it was offered to him by the Israeli government. Einstein wasn't Israeli but he was born Jewish, which qualified him for citizenship of the nation. He admitted he was flattered but rejected the offer, saying that he could only deal with objective matters such as science. Politics involved too much subjectivity. Right again, Einstein.

* * *

The first nation to give all adult women the right to vote in national elections was New Zealand, in 1893; the last – at least in large liberal democracies – was Switzerland, astonishingly as late as 1971, although Portugal, under military rule at the time, did not allow full female suffrage until 1975, and Spain only had it restored in 1976, following the fall of dictator Francisco Franco. The principality of Liechtenstein, however, held out until 1984.

The Cook Islands also gave women the vote in 1893, but after New Zealand. However, the Cook Islands held elections before New Zealand did and so women actually voted there first on 14 October, the first national election in the world where all adults could vote.

South Africa only enacted full suffrage in 1994 as a consequence of apartheid laws banning black people from voting for the previously whites-only government.

The Vatican City State is the only nation in the world where women cannot vote. However, in Saudi Arabia and Afghanistan it is impossible for a woman to exercise a decision, political or otherwise, without male permission. According to World Population Review, it is also considered difficult for some women to vote in Pakistan, Zanzibar, Papua New Guinea, Nigeria, Uganda, Kenya, Oman, Egypt, Qatar, and Nigeria.

Other examples of woefully late emancipation:

English law: Women were only legally granted equal pay for doing the same job as men in 1970.

England's Football Association: It outlawed women's football until 1971.

The Automobile Club de l'Ouest: The organisers of the Le Mans 24 Hour race decided in 1957 that it was too dangerous for women. The ban was only lifted in 1971.

The British banking system: Before the Equal Credit Opportunity Act of 1974 was passed, women were not allowed to open bank accounts and get credit cards without the permission of their husband or a male relative.

Magdalene College, Cambridge University: Only accepted female students in 1988.

The Marylebone Cricket Club (MCC) at Lord's: Only allowed women into its pavilion's famed Long Room in 1999 (although Queen Elizabeth II had an exception).

The Royal and Ancient Golf Club at St Andrews in Scotland: Only allowed women members in 2014.

Saudi Arabia: Only allowed women to drive in 2018.

The Constitution of the United States: Even today this still does not guarantee women the same rights and protections as men. It contains no explicit protection against discrimination on the basis of sex. The Equal Rights Amendment first proposed in 1923 has still to become law.

Formula 1: Out of almost 800 drivers who have started a Formula 1 World Championship Grand Prix, only two have been female. That's around 0.25% of the total. The first was Maria Teresa de Fillipis, an Italian aristocrat who started three races in the 1950s. The second was another Italian, Lella Lombardi, who started 12 races between 1974 and 1976 and is the only woman to score a point in the championship.

The Rwandan parliament's lower house consists of 61.3% women, making it the nation with the highest proportion of female representatives. The European country with the highest proportion of women in parliament is Iceland, with 47.6%.

Voting is compulsory for all or some sections of the electorate in: Argentina, Australia, Austria, Belgium, Bolivia, Brazil, Chile, Costa Rica, Cyprus, Democratic Republic of Congo, Ecuador, Egypt, Fiji, Greece, Honduras, Italy, Liechtenstein (ironically), Luxembourg, Mexico, Nauru, North Korea, Paraguay, Peru, Pitcairn Islands, Samoa, Singapore, Switzerland, Thailand, Turkey, and Uruguay. In some of these nations the law is only infrequently enforced.

Sweden was the first country in the world to offer paid parental leave in 1974. There is no federal statutory right to paid parental leave in the United States. There are six other nations who do not mandate paid parental leave:

Papua New Guinea, the Marshall Islands, Micronesia, Nauru, Palau, and Tonga.

Only two nations reserve places in their parliamentary legislatures for religious leaders: the Islamic Republic of Iran and the United Kingdom. The latter appoints 26 unelected bishops, plus all retired archbishops, to the House of Lords.

These five nominees won the majority of the votes cast but, because of the complex nature of the electoral college system used to elect the president of the United States, did not come to power: Andrew Jackson in 1824, Samuel Tilden in 1876, Grover Cleveland in 1888, Al Gore in 2000, and Hillary Clinton in 2016.

Similarly, because of its first-past-the-post system, the United Kingdom can elect a government that has received fewer votes than its main opposition. This happened most infamously in 1951, when more people – a quarter of a million – voted Labour than Conservative, but the Conservatives gained a 17-seat majority. It happened the other way around in 1974, when Labour won four more seats than the Conservatives, despite the latter receiving 200,000 more votes than the former.

France always votes on a Sunday. Shops are closed, restaurants notably empty, nothing happens. Which is why the government decided that to keep up voter turnout, Sundays it had to be, because people had little else to do.

Politicians with memorable names:

Butch Otter (former governor of Idaho)

Young Boozer (Alabama state treasurer)

Fretcheville (sometimes spelt Fretchville or Frecheville) Lawson Ballantine Dykes (former MP for Cockermouth)

Tiny Kox (Dutch politician)

Krystal Ball (a defeated candidate in the 2010 US elections – surely she knew she'd lose?)

Cresswell Cresswell (former MP for Liverpool)

Dutch prime minister Johan de Witt was, in 1672, one of the few non-royal national leaders in Europe. Unfortunately, his warlike tendencies displeased his people and, alongside his brother, he became one of very few politicians to be killed, have his liver roasted, and then have it eaten by those who voted him in.

These leaders and politicians all survived assassination attempts:

Abraham Lincoln, president-elect of the United States (failed assassin: Baltimore Plotters, year: 1861)

Edward, Prince of Wales (Jean Baptiste Sipido, 1900)

Grigori Rasputin, monk, advisor to Tsar Nicolas II (Khioniya Guseva, 1914)

Adolf Hitler, Nazi dictator (Claus Schenk, Graf von Stauffenberg, 1944)

Martin Luther King Jr, civil rights activist (Izola Curry, 1958)

Ronald Reagan, president of the United States (John Hinckley Jr, 1981)

Imran Khan, former cricketer, former prime minister of Pakistan (Muhammad Naveed, 2022)

It is subjective, but perhaps the worst political slogan was the Australian Liberal Party's 2016 effort "Continuity and Change", which contradicted itself in the space of three words.

And the most boring? "A Britain living within its means", used by the Conservative Party in 2015.

If you think insults are something common to modern politics, you'd be wrong. The following were all levelled at opponents in the 1800 US presidential election: "a bastard brat of a Scotch peddler" and "a hideous hermaphroditical character with neither the force or firmness of a man, nor the gentleness and sensibility of a woman." They weren't very politically correct in those days.

Meanwhile in Britain, Winston Churchill was always scathing of his political rival, Clement Attlee: "A very modest man. Indeed, he has much to be modest about," or "A sheep in sheep's clothing."

In the 1884 US presidential election, newspapers ran features comparing and analysing the skull shapes of the candidates. The now-discredited practice of phrenology declared that a person's character and mental ability could be determined by the shape of their head.

In 1918, Socialist Party candidate Eugene Debs ran his US presidential campaign from prison. Could such a thing ever happen again?

In the 1960 European Football Championship, Spain were drawn to play a quarter-final against the Soviet Union. But Spanish premier Francisco Franco was a fascist, who had not forgotten that Soviet aid was given to his republican opponents in the Spanish Civil War in 1936 that brought him to power. He feared defeat might re-open wounds among those who still opposed him, especially when the Soviet flag would have been flown over the stadium in Madrid. So instead of playing, Spain conceded the tie.

According to Amnesty International, China executes the most people in the world but the figure is a closely guarded state secret. It is believed to run into the thousands. Iran is second (it executed 576 people in 2022), followed by Saudi Arabia (196). Alone among western liberal democracies, the United States executed 18 people in 2022.

The lowest number of worldwide executions on record occurred during 2020 and 2021, the years of the Covid-19 pandemic.

Five countries are ruled by governments who describe themselves as communist. They are China, Cuba, Laos, North Korea, and Vietnam.

The US state of Alabama has a law which makes it illegal to wear a fake moustache in church if the moustache makes the rest of the congregation laugh.

The following laws were all still on the statute books in Britain at the start of the 21st century:

Mince pies cannot be eaten on Christmas Day (inveterate puritan Oliver Cromwell banned them, along with plum pudding).

It is illegal to die in the Houses of Parliament (apparently because the government has to grant you an expensive state funeral), and nor can you enter Parliament wearing a suit of armour.

Pregnant women can relieve themselves in public (fair enough, seeing as men are always doing it).

It is treasonable to put a postage stamp on a letter upside down (apparently it displeases the monarch to see their head the wrong way round).

You cannot be drunk in a pub.

All of which lead us nicely onto our myth busting section:

MYTH BUSTING

Myth: In Chester, you can shoot a Welshman after midnight, as long as you use a longbow.

A similar story does the rounds in Hereford. There you can only shoot the Welshman on a Sunday and only while you are in Cathedral Close. But Welshmen can heave a sigh of relief, neither story is true. Both narratives may have arisen from a curfew that was imposed on Welsh people following the Glyndwr Rising of 1403. But in neither city was murder ever encouraged. A similar myth exists in York, except this time it's Scots who are in the archers' sights.

Myth: John F. Kennedy told Berliners he was a "jam doughnut".

On June 26, 1963, US president John F. Kennedy told a crowd at the Berlin Wall: "Ich bin ein Berliner." He meant to say in German that he too was a citizen of their city, then divided by the Berlin Wall. Some critics claimed that by adding the indefinite article *ein* (or "a" in English) he actually called himself a jelly doughnut, known in much of Germany as a *Berliner*. However, German linguists say that the president did not make an error, firstly because German grammar demands that *ein* is required when the speaker is speaking figuratively about coming from a nation or place. More significantly the jam-filled pastry known as a *Berliner* in the rest of Germany is called a *Pfannkuchen* in Berlin, so there would have been no confusion among his audience.

Myth: Countries with McDonald's don't declare war on each other.

In 1996 political writer Thomas Friedman put forward his Golden Arches Theory of Conflict Prevention, which said that no two countries with a McDonald's have ever gone to war. This is because countries that can "sustain a McDonald's have reached a level of prosperity and global integration that makes warmongering risky and unpalatable to its people". He was proved wrong first with the break-up of former Yugoslavia, which had branches of McDonald's and was bombed by NATO forces including the US, the birthplace of McDonald's, in 1999. And most recently, Russia and Ukraine, both which have McDonald's branches, have been at war since February 2022.

Myth: Brexit has produced innumerable benefits for the British people.

Come on . . . Do you really think for one second we'd even go near this?

CHAPTER 18

HUMAN BODIES

Do our souls weigh anything?

In 1907 Duncan MacDougall, a physician in Massachusetts, weighed six people as they died to figure out how much a human soul weighed as it departed the body. He reckoned it was 21 grams but, oddly enough, no one has successfully repeated the experiment. Of course, much of this depends on whether you believe humans have a soul (so maybe this story should feature in our chapter on religion instead), but presumably MacDougall did and he reckoned he saw a downtick of the weighing needle as the person died. His sample size was very small, which rather brings the results into question. And plonking dying people on scales is, of course, a rather questionable practice and the authorities took a dim view of his methods, deeming it disrespectful and putting a stop to his experiments.

He still believed in his work, though, undeterred by the fact that for some subjects, the weight change occurred immediately, others after a short hiatus, saying: "The soul's weight is removed from the body virtually at the instant of the last breath, though in persons of sluggish temperament, it may remain in the body for a full minute", which sounds like making the facts fit your beliefs.

When no more humans were forthcoming, MacDougall switched to dogs. Very few religions believe dogs have souls and it seems that maybe they are correct. MacDougall reported that the dogs did not change weight when they died.

Ninety years later, though, a rancher in Oregon suggested replicating the experiment using sheep. He had a taker. Lewis E. Hollander Jr, a physicist, tried again using seven ewes, a ram, three lambs, and a goat. Apparently, this time the scales ticked up at the point of death. Did they gain a soul? Again, this is all anecdotal.

Intrigued (but presumably simultaneously disapproving), a group of priests from South America wrote to MacDougall to know if there was a difference in weight between those souls that ascended into heaven and those condemned to hell, hoping to be able to calculate the respective weights of the two afterlives and discover how many souls dwelt in each. History does not record whether MacDougall thought they were taking the mickey.

* * *

Our bodies are covered in invisible patterns known as Blaschko's lines, groups of cells that traverse our bodies. They are thought to represent pathways of epidermal cell migration and proliferation during the development of the foetus and only become obvious following some skin pigmentation diseases such as segmental vitiligo, where skin loses colour in patches across the body. They were named after Alfred Blaschko, a German dermatologist who first identified and drew the patterns in 1901.

You'll notice that the skin of your lips differs from that of the rest of your body. It is thinner, more flexible and has no sweat glands or hair follicles so that it can form an effective seal when you are drinking. Lips are also more sensitive so that we can detect when something is too hot or cold and might damage our intestines.

Persistent nose-picking is known as rhinotillexomania. Just because your forefinger fits your nostril perfectly, that is no excuse.

The French Emperor Napoleon Bonaparte was 5 feet 6 inches, or 1 metre 67.5 centimetres tall, around the average height for men at the time.

Close your eyes and rub them, and you'll see flashes of light known as phosphenes. You can even press different parts of your eyeball and see different colours. When you rub your eye, the pressure activates cells in your retina the same way light does. Your brain can't tell the difference and interprets the signal as though you were seeing real light. But don't rub too hard, your eyeballs are very sensitive . . .

And if your eyes are blue, pay attention: your eyes aren't really blue at all. You can find out elsewhere in this book why the sky is blue (see page 151). And the same thing causes blue eyes. When light hits the translucent surface of your eyes, it is scattered, just as it is when it hits the Earth's atmosphere and as it would be if it was striking a prism. Blue is scattered more than other colours and therefore becomes predominant. In the sky, it's known as Rayleigh scattering but in your eyes, it's called the Tyndall effect.

Fingernails grow on average three times as fast as toenails, at 3.47 millimetres a month. In some people the rate can be four times as fast.

When Beulah Hunter gave birth to her daughter Penny in Los Angeles on 21 February, 1945, it concluded the longest pregnancy on record: 375 days, or around 100 days overdue. The record is unlikely to be beaten because today most births are induced if the mother is more than two weeks overdue. In 2016, a woman in China announced she had a longer pregnancy but doctors were unable to verify her claim.

Babies are born with around 300 bones. Adults only have 206. Bones fuse as you age and cartilage between a baby's bones ossifies into more bone, creating one bone from two.

The largest bone in the human body is the femur, or thigh bone.

The smallest bone is the stirrup bone, found in your eardrum.

Humans have the same number of bones in their necks as giraffes – seven.

Human bone is about five times stronger by weight than steel.

It takes between 45 and 60 seconds for your blood to make a complete lap of your body. Unless you are running fast and then, like you, it speeds up.

If your blood vessels were removed and laid end to end, they would stretch around the world more than three times.

If you live until 70, your heart will beat around 2.5 billion times.

Humans make on average about 30,000 litres of spit in a lifetime.

The surface of your skin is replaced every month, although this slows as you age. Every minute you shed around 30,000 dead skin cells.

According to *Scientific American,* every day your body produces 330 billion new cells, the equivalent of 1% of all the cells in your body. In 30 minutes, you will have produced more cells than there are people in the world.

Humans have three times as many hair follicles (around five million) as a gorilla. Only your palms, soles, and lips don't have them.

Stomach acid can burn human skin and dissolve razor blades (outside the body).

Bacteria, which like the warm, damp conditions inside your socks and trainers, are usually the cause of smelly feet. However, there also is an inherited condition called bromidrosis. In this case, the sweat your feet emit has a natural, if very unpleasant, smell like mouldy cheese and overboiled cabbage. If, unfortunately, you have it, regular washing with antibacterial soap is your best option.

You can't sneeze in your sleep. Sleep causes paralysis of the reflex muscle contraction, meaning the relevant muscles become inactive. However, the urge to sneeze may wake you, meaning that you might suddenly awake to find yourself sneezing.

Cannibals report that the meat humans most taste like is pig. In parts of the Pacific region, human meat was known as "long pork".

MYTH BUSTING

Myth: Humans only use 10% of their brains.

This myth has become rooted in popular culture and is always accompanied by the declaration that, if only we could use the other 90%, we'd become superhuman. It's probably arisen because the 10% refers only to the amount of brain tissue that we need to function normally, suggesting, erroneously, that the other 90% is sitting there redundant and unused and, if it were removed, we'd not notice any difference. This is wrong. In fact, we use pretty much all of our brains, the rest being a mixture of fats, water, proteins, carbohydrates, and salts. Scans show that our entire brain is active, even when we are sleeping. Different tasks use different parts of the brain and operate in different ways. For example, the part that stores our memories is not linked to the parts that enable us to walk or catch a ball, and it's probably the capacity of this latter part of the brain that leads to the 10% pronouncement. And if 90% of our brains could be removed without us noticing, then brain damage would be far less catastrophic than we know it to be.

In 1848 Vermont railway worker Phineas Gage was struck by a tamping iron. The metre-long projectile passed through his cheek, brain, and skull and landed 25 metres away. Amazingly, he survived and returned to work, despite losing an estimated 20% of his brain. But it changed his character from affable to grumpy.

Intelligence in mammals is linked to the surface area of their brains. The human brain has folds and fissures in it to increase this surface area because a lot of the important work it undertakes takes place in the top few layers of cells.

Mammals that are less intelligent, such as rats, have smooth brains.

A large surface area also allows the vast amount of heat the brain generates to be more easily released. (Similarly, the human scrotum is wrinkled in order to have a greater surface area from which heat can dissipate to keep the testicles cool. Sperm flourish better at cooler temperatures.)

In 2010 *Scientific American* suggested that, although it was very difficult to calculate the storage capacity of the human brain, it was possibly in the region of a million gigabytes (enough to hold three million hours of YouTube videos). When you can't find where you put your glasses, this is likely to be of little consolation.

Our brain accounts for 2% of our body mass, but uses 20% of the oxygen in our blood supply.

Myth: Hair and fingernails continue to grow when you die.

No, they don't. What happens is your body starts to dry out, meaning it shrinks and the skin around your hair and nails begins to recede, merely giving the impression of growth. Funeral parlours deliberately hydrate corpses with moisturiser to reduce the effect.

Myth: Ears continue to grow throughout your life.

They don't, but they do appear to get larger. That's because they are made of cartilage, which contains collagen and other fibres that break down as we age, at which point gravity starts having an effect by dragging down the collagen. Our earlobes sag and become larger. Noses are also affected in a similar way.

Myth: Carrots are good for eyesight.

They do contain beta carotene, which the body uses to help make vitamin A, which in turn helps nourish our eyes, but the story that they improve eyesight was a myth put about by Britain's Air Ministry during the Second World War. Relying on the newly invented radar to detect where the German planes were, British pilots were getting good strike rates in their night-time dogfights with German aircraft. The Air Ministry didn't want the enemy to know the secret of their success, so they invented the decoy carrots story.

Myth: Some people have photographic memories.

There's no doubt that some people have better memories than others, but it has never been proved that some individuals can read a book and then recall with clarity the exact words on every page, which would be the definition of a photographic memory. Memory for detail, in any case, tends to come with practice. Those who can identify faces or paintings are often people intimately involved in such fields, such as border force officials or art historians. And even these people have to draw up shopping lists or stick reminders on their fridge doors.

Myth: Man flu isn't real.

Annoyingly for women tired of hearing how much men suffer when they have what would be to them a minor head cold, "man flu" is a genuine thing. A Harvard University study linked high levels of oestrogen to a better immune response. Oestrogen is one of the main female sex hormones. So when it comes to the ability to fight off cold and flu viruses, men fare badly. And once they do catch them, they feel the effects more seriously.

It's also likely to be true that you catch a cold the moment you stop work to go on annual leave. It's known as "leisure sickness". Dutch psychologists Maaike van Huijgevoort and Ad Vingerhoets questioned nearly 2000 people in 2002, 3% of whom said as soon as they finished work, they went down with a nasty cold. This is subjective, of course, but far higher than the percentage who might otherwise get ill. The theory is the stress hormones that help you deal with the looming deadlines just before you stop work leave you open to infection, while the associated adrenaline kick, which helps boost the immune system, disappears the moment you relax. Cortisol is also produced by the adrenal glands in stressful situations and creating too much of it can cause health issues.

The Dutch psychologists noted the similarity of leisure sickness to so-called paradise syndrome, in which sufferers feel dissatisfaction with their lives despite having achieved all their goals and dreams.

CHAPTER 19

THE OLYMPIC GAMES

Spyridon Louis gets a new water cart.

The first marathon was run in 1896 at the inaugural modern Olympic Games in Athens. It was won by Spyridon Louis, who, in his home village of Marousi, was employed as a water carrier, having previously been in the Greek army. It was Greece's only gold medal of the games and it was won in the very last event. The king of Greece bought him a new water cart as a prize.

That first marathon was only 24.85 miles (40 kilometres) (the distance between the town of Marathon and the Olympic Stadium in Athens). Marathon was chosen as the starting point because of the legend of Pheidippides, a Greek messenger. In 490 BC he was sent from the battlefield of Marathon to Athens to announce that the Persians had been defeated. It is said that he ran the entire distance without stopping and burst into the assembly, exclaiming, "We have won" before collapsing and dying. Inspired by the legend, French academic Michel Bréal suggested to the founder of the modern Olympics, Baron Pierre de Coubertin, that a long-distance race be run over the same course.

At the 1904 Olympics in St Louis the favourites were Americans Frederick Lorz and Thomas Hicks. Lorz dropped out injured early on, took a car to the stadium in St Louis and jogged in to pick up his kit bags. He was hailed as the winner and decided to say nothing. Later his deceitfulness was uncovered and victory went to Hicks, who had fuelled his run on a mixture of brandy and the often-deadly poison strychnine, neither of which were illegal at the time.

By 1908 the marathon was being run over courses of up to 26 miles (41.84 kilometres) but at the Olympic Games in London that year, Queen Alexandra wanted the race to finish in front of her royal box. This meant the course was extended by 385 yards (352 metres). It proved the undoing of Italian Dorando Pietri. Exhausted and dehydrated, he entered the stadium first but collapsed agonisingly short of the line. Officials supported him and he crossed the line but was disqualified for receiving outside assistance. He is still remembered today, unlike the official winner, American Johnny Hayes.

26 miles 385 yards (42.19 kilometres) is now the official distance of the marathon. Presumably, Dorando Pietri wishes it wasn't.

Ethiopian Abebe Bikila is the only athlete to win an Olympic title running barefoot. He won the marathon in Rome in 1960.

The first woman to win an Olympic marathon was Joan Benoit of the USA, who won the inaugural women's title at the 1984 Los Angeles games.

A marathon runner's feet hit the ground around 60,000 times during the race.

* * *

The ancient Olympic Games were held in Olympia in the Greek Peloponnese from at least 776 BC. Like now, they were held every four years and attracted competitors from across Greece, plus the Roman and Macedonian empires. Only men could compete.

The ancient games were considered so sacred that for their duration all hostilities between nations and states were ceased. When the city-state of Sparta broke this truce it was fined the equivalent of a million dollars today.

Athletes competed in the nude – even in events such as horse riding and wrestling – their muscular physiques considered a tribute to the Greek God Zeus. The English word "gymnasium" is derived from the Greek word *gymnos,* which means "naked or lightly clad".

When Emperor Nero of Rome attended in 67 AD (having postponed the games for a year so he could compete), he brought 5000 bodyguards with him and, perhaps rather unsurprisingly, won every event in which he participated.

The first man to win an Olympic title (or at least the first in 1500 years since the ancient Olympics were last contested) was American James Connolly, who won the triple jump on 6 April, 1896 at the first modern Olympic Games in Athens. Women weren't allowed to compete until 1900.

Coroebus, however, might disagree. The cook from the Greek province of Elis was the first recorded winner of an event at the ancient Olympics, a footrace held at Olympia in 776 BC.

At the first modern Olympics in Athens in 1896, the swimming races took place in the sea. Competitors were taken out by boats to the correct distance for their event and were expected to swim back to shore in waves of up to a metre high. Hungarian Alfred Hajos who won two events was quoted as saying, "My will to live completely overcame my desire to win."

The first woman to win a modern Olympic title was Britain's Charlotte Cooper, who, on 11 July, won the women's tennis singles at the Paris games of 1900. She was already a three-time Wimbledon champion and went on to win gold in the mixed doubles.

Gold medals for Olympic champions weren't awarded until the St Louis games of 1904. Previously they had been considered too expensive.

London is the only city to host three summer Olympic Games: 1908, 1948, and 2012.

From 1912 to 1948, the Olympic Games held competitions in the fine arts. Medals were given for literature, architecture, sculpture, painting, and music.

American high jumper Harold Osborn won gold in 1924 at the Paris games. He had learnt the technique of pushing the bar back onto its supports if he knocked it off while passing over it. The practice was subsequently outlawed.

The first-ever 800 metres for women at the 1928 Amsterdam Olympics led to the event being outlawed for 32 years. It was won by German Lina Radke in a world record time but the fact that some women looked exhausted at the end of the race seemed to upset many watching. British newspaper the *Daily Telegraph* wrote, "To run roughly half a mile at breakneck speed is surely too much for any girl," while the *Daily Mail* reported doctors as saying that such feats of endurance would make a woman "become old too soon". The *Daily Express* pointed out that women are apt to "cry when they win, and cry when they are beaten". Astonishingly, the International Olympic Committee paid attention to such tosh and no women's events over 200 metres were held until the 1960 games in Rome.

At the 1932 games in Los Angeles, officials showed American Ralph Metcalfe to the wrong starting mark in the final of the men's 200 metres. This meant he started a metre and a half behind all the other competitors yet still won the bronze medal. He sportingly refused the offer of a rerun.

When Tommie Smith and John Carlos of the USA made a Black Power salute in support of the civil rights move-ment after coming first and third in the 200 metres at the 1968 Olympics, they were banned from competition. But so was Peter Norman, the White Australian who finished second. Norman refused to condemn the actions of Smith and Carlos as they stood on the victory podium. The two Americans were so impressed by Norman's action that they became friends and acted as pallbearers at his funeral.

At those 1968 games in Mexico, Bob Beamon broke the world and Olympic record in the men's long jump at 8.90 metres. It is still the Olympic record today.

Only two athletes have died at Olympic Games while competing in their events: Portuguese marathon runner Francisco Lázaro in Stockholm in 1912, and Danish cyclist Knud Enemark Jensen in Rome in 1960. Both suffered from heat stroke.

Another six athletes have died in practice for their sports or shortly after competing and in 1972 at the Munich Olympics, 11 members of the Israeli Olympic team were killed by the terrorist organisation Black September.

In the 1984 games in Los Angeles, the Puerto Rican 4 x 400-metre relay athlete Madeline de Jesus injured herself competing in the long jump. Her twin sister Margaret, only there as a spectator, replaced her in the relay team, which reached the final before the deceit was discovered.

Olympic and world-champion athlete Gail Devers had fingernails that were 10 centimetres long. It had taken her three years to recover from Graves' disease, during which time she never cut her nails. Instead of using her fingertips, she had to balance on her knuckles while in her starting blocks.

Briton Roald Bradstock, a former Olympic javelin thrower, holds the world record for throwing a snowball. He made the snowballs in Atlanta, Georgia after a snowstorm in January, 2010, and drove them 600 miles to Fort Myers, Florida, where the record was set and verified at 68.1 metres.

For the first time in Olympic history, at the 2012 London games every competing nation sent at least one female athlete.

At the 2016 Olympic Games in Rio de Janeiro, organisers ordered 450,000 condoms for the athletes. That worked out at 42 per competitor.

Czech skier Ester Ledecka had never finished in the top three of a Super-G slalom event. In fact, she was better known as a snowboarder but, in the Pyeongchang Winter Olympics of 2018, she borrowed a pair of skis to simply take part in the Super-G, hoping to aid her recovery from injury. She was expected to finish last but won gold. As officials took her to the podium, she was still saying, "There must be some mistake."

Michael Phelps, the American swimmer, has the most Olympic medals, 28 in total. He has 23 gold medals (14 more than his nearest challenger), three silver, and two bronze.

The country with the most summer Olympic medals in total is the United States, with 2656. It is followed by the Soviet Union (1010 – with Russia winning an additional 425), Great Britain & Northern Ireland (916), and France (750).

Adding in Winter Olympic medals still sees the USA top the table with 2980.

San Marino, with three medals and a population of 34,000, tops the table if countries are ranked per head of population.

Italian Gianmarco Tamberi and Qatari Mutaz Barshim were heading into a jump-off for the 2021 Tokyo Olympic high-jump title. They were also good friends, so they asked if they could share the gold medal. Officials said yes and they became the first athletes to share an Olympic track-and-field title since 1912, when Hugo Weislander from Sweden and the US athlete Jim Thorpe shared first place in the decathlon, as did Ferdinand Reinhardt Bie from Norway and, once again, Thorpe in the pentathlon.

MYTH BUSTING

Myth: You have to be an amateur to compete at the Olympics.

Originally this was the case. The founder of the modern games Baron Pierre de Coubertin was greatly influenced by the aristocratic ethos behind the English public-school system that saw sport as a fundamental part of what was called Muscular Christianity. This decreed that God should be served through mental and physical effort and saw accepting cash for sporting endeavour as vulgar. Many Olympic athletes were stripped of their medals when it was discovered they had accepted payment for competing, even elsewhere. But today professionals can compete alongside amateur sportspeople as long as they don't accept money while at the Olympics.

In 1912 Jim Thorpe of the USA was stripped of his pentathlon and decathlon medals (see earlier in this chapter) because he had been found to have played semi-professional baseball. In 1983 the International Olympic Committee relented and reinstated him.

In 1936 Austrian and Swiss skiers were banned from the Winter Olympics simply for having been ski instructors which "professionalised" them.

CHAPTER 20

LIFE AS WE KNOW IT

The burning issue of the Gävle Goat.

Every Christmas the town of Gävle in Sweden erects a goat in its main square. And every year it is burnt down. Well, nearly every year. Of the 57 goats built since 1966, 38 have been destroyed or damaged. And most of the time nobody knows who the perpetrator was. Straw goats are common at Yuletide across Sweden but none has been targeted in the way Gävle's has. Cameras, security guards, dogs, and a fireproof coating seem simply to add to the challenge. Although mostly the goat has been set on fire, in 1973 one man simply turned up with a truck and stole it. In 1976 a student drove his car into it. In 1988 book-makers started taking bets on its fate. In 2005 all the security cameras managed to pick up were flaming arrows landing on the goat's back. Despite 38 successful goat destructions only four people have been prosecuted. One was an American man who, in 2001, argued in court that he thought burning the goat down was a completely legal tradition and he was trying to uphold it. He spent 18 days in jail. In recent years the goat has fared better but in 2021 the arsonists succeeded again. Doubtless it will be built again this year (and every subsequent year), and doubtless somebody, somewhere will be buying matches.

* * *

Why do we keep money in pigs? One story has it that because pigs symbolised wealth and prosperity in Chinese culture, people started making pig-shaped vessels to store their money in. Another says it comes from the Saxon tradition of placing any spare coins in a clay pot called a pygg. Because the word was similar to the animal's name, eventually potters began making clay pigs to store the coins in.

People talk of sweating like a pig. Which is odd, because pigs, real or pottery, can't sweat. Pigs can't fly either.

Pigs will eat almost anything, including humans, as the family of an unfortunate farmer from Oregon who had a heart attack while cleaning his pig sty discovered in 2012. Pigs in California also tried to eat a camera being used to film a parachute jump that fell into their sty from an aircraft.

One man who needed a very big piggy bank was the subject of a famous music-hall song. And it seems the

"Man who broke the bank at Monte Carlo", made famous by Fred Gilbert's music-hall song, was not fictitious. Most likely he was Joseph Hobson Jagger, a textile businessman from Brighouse in West Yorkshire, who had fallen on hard times. During his work with looms, he realised that all machines that spin have a bias and tend to stop at the same point in their cycle. Rightly figuring that roulette wheels must do the same, in 1880 he scraped his last pennies together, headed to the famous casino in Monaco, watched where the roulette wheels stopped most frequently, and cleaned up. Don't try Jagger's plan today. Casinos are far better at balancing their wheels and regularly switch them between tables. You'll lose . . .

The casino at Monte Carlo is one of the most photographed buildings in the world. But the most photographed structure of all is the Eiffel Tower in Paris.

The most photographed clock in the world is Big Ben (it's also the second most photographed structure). Big Ben is the name of the great bell inside what is properly called the Elizabeth Tower.

The rights to the game Monopoly in the UK were bought in 1935 by Waddington's in Leeds, 200 miles north of London. Victor Watson, Waddington's managing director, decided to make the game more Anglocentric by changing its original New York street names to London's. He despatched his secretary Marjory Phillips to the capital. She stayed in a hotel overlooking Vine Street, a quiet dead end near Piccadilly, which is why it appears on the board next to far more famous thoroughfares.

The only square on a standard UK Monopoly board that features a street south of the River Thames is Old Kent Road.

Many countries have Aldi supermarkets. But Germany's are divided into two: Aldi Nord and Aldi Sud. Brothers and owners Theo Jr and Bertholdt Albrecht split the business in 1960 when they fell out over whether to sell cigarettes or not. Theo was pro, Karl was anti. They drew a line across the middle of Germany, through their home town of Essen, and shared out the stores. If you live in the Netherlands, France, or Poland, you are an Aldi Nord shopper. If you live in the US, Britain, Ireland, Italy, or Australia, you are Aldi Sud.

The oldest registered trademark in the world is "Pilsner Bier" registered with the Czech patent office in 1859 by the original makers of the first pilsner or lager, the Pilsner Urquell brewery in Plzeň (see page 91).

The oldest registered trademark in the US is the Averill Ready-Mix Paint logo depicting an eagle, which dates back to 1870.

The oldest registered British trademark is the red triangle used by Bass beers since 1876. A Bass employee slept on the steps of the newly opened British Patent Office to ensure the company would be granted Britain's first trade-mark.

Freemasons – one of the oldest private membership organ-isations in the world – have at least 12 secret handshakes implemented in their society. However, it is believed the actual number may top 50.

The first public self-service Launderette opened on 18 April, 1934 in Fort Worth, Texas. It was called a Washateria.

China produces more wind power and more solar power than any other nation. The Gansu Wind Farm in China is the largest wind farm in the world. It will eventually have 7000 turbines.

It has been projected that to power the whole world 2.5 million wind turbines would be required.

The first telegram ever sent contained the words "What hath God wrought?" It was sent by the telegraph's inventor Samuel Morse – using, of course, Morse code – from Washington DC to Baltimore on 24 May, 1844.

The first mobile phone call was made on 3 April, 1973 by Motorola employee Martin Cooper, from Manhattan to the headquarters of Bell Laboratories in New Jersey.

The longest phone call, made by Eric Brewster and Avery Leonard, lasted for 46 hours, 12 minutes, 52 seconds, and

228 milliseconds in January, 2012. It was part of a perform-
ance art installation to publicise the Harvard Generalist,
a student arts cooperative at Harvard University.

The first text message was sent on 3 December, 1992 by
Neil Papworth, a British Vodaphone test engineer, to his
colleague Richard Jarvis. It said "Merry Christmas".

Today it is estimated that worldwide 23 billion texts a day
are sent – that's 270,000 every second.

The tallest building in the world in 1311 was Lincoln
Cathedral in England. It was (and still is) 159.7 metres
and held the record until 1549 (or 238 years), the longest
any building has remained the tallest.

Currently the tallest building in the world is the Burj
Khalifa in Dubai, United Arab Emirates, at 828 metres, a
record it has held for 13 years.

The tallest structure in the world, however, is the under-
water Magnolia oil platform in the Gulf of Mexico, at
1432 metres, 604 metres taller than the Burj Khalifa.

Sudan has more pyramids than Egypt.

The longest corridor in the world with no kinks or bends
is at Mount Pleasant Royal Air Force base in the Falkland
Islands. It is 800 metres long.

The longest escalators in the world are in the underground stations of the St Petersburg Metro. The Ploshchad Lenina, Chernishevskaya, and Admiralteyskaya stations have escalators 138 metres long and 69 metres high.

The shortest escalator in the world is in the Okadaya More's shopping mall in Kawasaki, Japan. Its rise is 83.2 centimetres and it has 5 steps. It also has a name – the "Puchicalator". *Puchi*, in Japanese, means "small".

The world's longest-lasting light bulb has been burning since 1901, and has hardly ever been turned off (which may account for its longevity). It is maintained by the Livermore-Pleasanton Fire Department in California. It even has a name: the Centennial light bulb.

The following are all real colours:

Smaragdine (a pale green).

Glaucous (a powder-blue/grey).

Goose Turd Green (speaks for itself. Apparently, it was very popular with Elizabethan dressmakers).

Drunk-Tank Pink (a pink colour painted in police cells to calm down the inebriated).

Caput Mortuum (it means "worthless remains" in Latin and is a purple-rust colour).

Puke (a brown shade named after the colours of stockings mentioned in Shakespeare, and not – as you might imagine – after vomit).

The longest word in English is 189,819 letters long (too long to print here) and takes up to three and a half hours to say. However, it is a technical word for the chemical composition of the protein titin, it does not appear in dictionaries, and there are disputes over whether it constitutes a real word.

The longest word that appears in a standard English dictionary is pneumonoultramicroscopicsilicovolcanoconiosis, the full name of the disease silicosis (which, for obvious reasons, is used far more often). It has 45 letters.

Discounting technical words, the language with the longest word is Sanskrit. A compound word of 195 characters (which translates to 428 letters in the Roman alphabet) is used to describe the region near Kanchi, Tamil Nadu, India in a 16th-century work by Tirumalamba, Queen of Vijayanagara.

The first triangular cardboard sandwich box, so common in supermarket meal deals today, was introduced by Marks & Spencer in 1979. Today the market is worth £10 billion annually and accounts for a third of all lunches eaten in the UK. Author Douglas Adams was not a fan. In *So Long, And Thanks for All the Fish* he wrote, "It is by eating sandwiches in pubs on Saturday lunchtimes that the

British seek to atone for whatever their national sins have been."

Air pockets in pre-packaged sandwiches caused by curved lettuce leaves are known as "goblin caves".

The tallest combined height for a married couple is 4 metres 77 centimetres. Anna Haining Swan was 2 metres 41 centimetres tall and her husband, Martin Van Buren Bates, 2 metres 36 centimetres.

MYTH BUSTING

Myth: There are no real cockneys because no one is born within the sound of Bow Bells any more.

To some outsiders, all Londoners are known as cockneys. But that's not the case. A real cockney is defined as a person born within hearing distance of the church bells of St Mary-le-Bow, Cheapside, in the City of London. Before the onset of modern levels of noise pollution, it was estimated that the sound of the Bow Bells reached about 10 kilometres east, 8 kilometres north, 6 kilometres west, and 5 kilometres south. Although hospitals still fall within this remit, traffic noise has dimmed the sound of the bells, and the area is far less residential than it once was. However, home births account for approximately 2.5% of all births in the UK, which means real cockneys, although fewer in number, are still being born. Meanwhile, St Mary-le-Bow Church will provide a recording of the sound of the bells for those of cockney descent around the world who might wish to play it during the birth of their children.

Cockney rhyming slang is used all over the English-speaking world, although many people using it might not realise it. The three most recognisable phrases are "apples and pears" for "stairs", "China [plate]" for "mate", and "loaf [of bread]" for "head".

Myth: Santa Claus wears a red coat because Coca-Cola wanted to use him in their advertising.

Santa Claus – or Father Christmas – originally wore coats in a variety of colours, mostly in shades of green or red. The traditional religious robes of the original 3rd-century St Nicholas, the bishop of Myra in Turkey – on whom Santa Claus is based – were predominantly red. He also had a habit of buying secret gifts for worthy members of his flock. However, it is fair to say that Coca-Cola's depiction of Santa in its adverts played heavily on the colour which matched their brand and, by the late 1930s, he was always dressed exclusively in red.

Coca-Cola's adverts also helped transform Santa into the rotund, smiling character we recognise today after Swedish-American artist Haddon Sundblom was commissioned in 1931 to create a Santa for Coca-Cola's Christmas campaign. Prior to this, he'd been variously depicted as tall, thin, gaunt, intellectual, and sometimes rather scary-looking. Not someone you'd want to come down your chimney.

Myth: Denim was invented in America.

We most usually associate blue jeans and double-denim wearers with Stetsons and the United States. But the clue is in the name. The fabric takes its name from the town of Nîmes in southern France, an important textile town since the 17th century. *De Nîmes* means "from Nîmes".

ACKNOWLEDGEMENTS

Thanks are due to:

Alun Anderson
Katie Bond
Laura Fletcher
Andrew Franklin
Alice Grandison
Polly Halsey
Ben Longstaff
Ian Manders
Sally Manders
Teasel Muir-Harmony
Thomas O'Hare
Juliette Rudelle
Christopher Sherwood

Bedford Square Publishers

Bedford Square Publishers is an independent publisher of fiction and non-fiction, founded in 2022 in the historic streets of Bedford Square London and the sea mist shrouded green of Bedford Square Brighton.

Our goal is to discover irresistible stories and voices that illuminate our world.

We are passionate about connecting our authors to readers across the globe and our independence allows us to do this in original and nimble ways.

The team at Bedford Square Publishers has years of experience and we aim to use that knowledge and creative insight, alongside evolving technology, to reach the right readers for our books. From the ones who read a lot, to the ones who don't consider themselves readers, we aim to find those who will love our books and talk about them as much as we do.

We are hunting for vital new voices from all backgrounds – with books that take the reader to new places and transform perceptions of the world we live in.

Follow us on social media for the latest Bedford Square Publishers news.

@bedsqpublishers
facebook.com/bedfordsq.publishers/
@bedfordsq.publishers

https://bedfordsquarepublishers.co.uk/